Twayne's English Authors Series

Sylvia E. Bowman, *Editor*

INDIANA UNIVERSITY

Thomas Kyd

Thomas Kyd

By PETER B. MURRAY

Macalester College

Twayne Publishers, Inc.   ::   New York

For my children:
Jean, Stephen, Susan,
and Christopher

Preface

"SPORTING KYD" is such an interesting writer that we wish we knew more surely what he wrote.[1] We know he was the author of *The Spanish Tragedy*, that most seminal of all Elizabethan plays, only because Thomas Heywood casually mentioned the fact long after the play was already famous. We also know that he translated Robert Garnier's academic Senecan play, *Cornelia*, from the French, and Tasso's *The Householder's Philosophy* from the Italian. He may have been the "T.K." who was responsible for a journalistic pamphlet about *The Murder of John Brewen*. There is also some reason to believe he wrote the original version of *Hamlet*, but that play does not survive.

Because Kyd is an important writer but has few works that we can be certain he wrote, scholars have tried to find evidence of his authorship in the many anonymous plays of the sixteenth century. Of the works attributed to Kyd, the most interesting are *Soliman and Perseda* and *Arden of Feversham*. I have made a close study of the language of these plays, however, and cannot convince myself that they are the work of the author of *The Spanish Tragedy*. Other plays that have been attributed to Kyd include the pre-Shakespearean *King Leir*, *The Troublesome Reign of King John*, *The Rare Triumphs of Love and Fortune*, *The First Part of Jeronimo*, and Shakespeare's *Titus Andronicus*. But these plays, too, differ in style and language from *The Spanish Tragedy*, and, in any case, most of them are so bad that one *hopes* Kyd did not write them. As a result, a book about Thomas Kyd turns out to be a book about *The Spanish Tragedy*. And this is as it should be: whatever else Kyd may have written, it is through this play and the lost *Hamlet*, if that work was his, that he had a great influence on his contemporaries. Of the other plays attributed to him, only *Arden of Feversham* can be recommended.

The plan of this book is designed to make my ideas about *The*

Spanish Tragedy clear and readily accessible to the reader. In the first chapter I discuss the background of the play and describe its structure in such a way as to discover the questions about it to which criticism must respond. In the second chapter I try to answer these questions, arguing that, through its complex intrigue, the play develops a truly tragic action. This chapter may be read by itself as an essay in the interpretation of the play. In the next five chapters I support the theses already set forth, analyzing the action of the play scene by scene. At the cost of occasionally repeating or referring back to material discussed in Chapter II, I have attempted to make the analysis of each scene complete so that the development of action, character, and theme will always be clear. The final chapter considers the play's relation to the tragic writing that followed it, with special attention to the additions to Kyd's play that were published in 1602.

I want to express my gratitude to the University of Pennsylvania for research grants that provided time for me to undertake this project. I am also indebted to Dr. William E. Miller of the Horace Howard Furness Memorial Library at the University of Pennsylvania and to Mrs. Delphine O. Richardson of the University of Pennsylvania Library for their assistance in my research. And I especially want to thank my friends Elizabeth J. Turner, Richard Wertime, and John Bernstein for reading the manuscript and making many helpful suggestions for its improvement.

PETER B. MURRAY

Macalester College

Contents

Chronology[2]

1558   Thomas Kyd baptized on November 6 in the church of St. Mary Woolnoth in London. His mother was Anna Kyd; his father, Francis Kyd, was an important member of the Company of Scriveners of London. We believe this Thomas Kyd to have been the playwright, but no document directly links the son of Francis Kyd with the author.

1564   Christopher Marlowe and William Shakespeare born.

1565   Thomas, the son of Francis Kyd, enrolled in the Merchant Taylors' School in London, which Edmund Spenser also attended. The headmaster, Richard Mulcaster, advocated writing serious works in English rather than Latin, and he trained his boys to perform plays at court.

There is no evidence that Kyd attended Oxford or Cambridge. He may have been a scrivener for a time.

1576   Blackfriars Theater in London and The Theater in Shoreditch opened as the first places in the London area to be used especially for the presentation of plays.

1581   The *Tenne Tragedies* of Seneca published in English.

1580– Plays of John Lyly, George Peele, Robert Greene, and
1594   Christopher Marlowe performed.

1587– Kyd served a lord who was patron of a group of players,
1593   probably Lord Strange or the Earl of Sussex.

1582– Probably after 1587 Kyd wrote *The Spanish Tragedy.*
1592

1588   Kyd translated Tasso's *Padre di Famiglia* as *The Householder's Philosophy.*

1589   Thomas Nashe wrote an obscure preface to Greene's *Menaphon* that may imply Kyd had written a play *Hamlet.*

1588– The earliest plays of Shakespeare produced.
1590

1591   Kyd and Marlowe wrote in one chamber, which may mean they shared lodgings.

1593   May 12: Kyd in prison in connection with public libels against foreigners. In a search of his lodgings, heretical writings were found. Kyd said, under torture, that these papers were the property of Marlowe. Kyd denied all wrongdoing.

1593   During the summer, Kyd wrote a letter to Sir John Puckering, the Lord Keeper, asking him to intercede for him with his patron, who had abandoned Kyd in his disgrace, although Kyd was evidently cleared of the charges against him.

1593   Between May and December Kyd translated Robert Garnier's *Cornelie* as *Cornelia*. In the dedication he complained of the "afflictions of the mind," "bitter times," and "broken passions" he had been suffering.

1594   The Parish Record of St. Mary Colchurch contains the following entry: "Thomas Kydd the sonne of ffrauncis Kydd was buryed the 15 day of August 1594."

1594   On December 30, Anna Kyd, acting for Francis, renounced the right to administer the estate of her deceased son Thomas, presumably because he left nothing but debts.

CHAPTER 1

Thomas Kyd and The Spanish Tragedy

I *Some Cultural Contexts*

THE reputation of Thomas Kyd as an important Elizabethan dramatist rests on one work, *The Spanish Tragedy*. This exciting revenge melodrama was in its own time the most notorious if not the most famous of all plays. More than forty years after its writing, Richard Brathwaite recorded the marvelous story of a dying woman who would not let her comforters prepare her soul for its great translation because she had a more pressing spiritual need: "Hieronimo, Hieronimo, O let me see Hieronimo acted!" [1] To the righteous Brathwaite, *The Spanish Tragedy* is an evil tempter; but for him, as for less moralistic critics who parodied it, the play had almost as great a fascination as it did for those who were led astray to the wicked playhouses.

Among those led astray were other dramatists, notably Shakespeare, John Marston, Cyril Tourneur, John Webster, Thomas Middleton, and John Ford. These writers were greatly influenced by many features of *The Spanish Tragedy* and its near twin, the original version of *Hamlet,* which was also probably written by Kyd. Since this early *Hamlet* has not come down to us, *The Spanish Tragedy* alone must satisfy our curiosity about the origins of the Elizabethan revenge play.[2]

The Spanish Tragedy combines elements of several literary and dramatic types to create a new formula having great potential for sensational and theatrical action, for exciting characters in extremes of emotion, and for dramatic speech that is at once passionate, philosophical, and artfully controlled (for a plot summary and analysis, see pp. 20–23). To create his new formula, Kyd drew on classical drama and epic and on their Renaissance imitations, on the Italian novella, and on the medieval and Tudor traditions of the morality and the interlude.

The Greek tragedies of Aeschylus, Sophocles, and Euripides

were little known in the Renaissance, but the adaptations of
their plays by the Roman Stoic philosopher and poet, Seneca,
were studied in the schools.[3] From Seneca, Kyd derived the spa-
cious rhetorical eloquence and the introspective philosophizing of
his soliloquies and also the concise sententiousness of his dialogue, especially in the passages of stichomythia, in which single
lines are spoken alternately by characters (e.g., I. iii. 45–51).[4]
But, above all, Seneca provided the theme of revenge and the
atmosphere of horror and of human subjection to an inexorable and murderous fate. Kyd modeled his induction and chorus of
Revenge and the ghost of Andrea on the opening of Seneca's
Thyestes, in which a Fury from the underworld drives the ghost
of Tantalus back to the world of the living in order to goad his
family on to new evil.

Because Seneca evidently wrote plays for declamation or reading more than for staging, the battles and murders in his tragedies
are described in great detail to permit the audience to visualize
the events it does not actually see. The emotions of the characters
also tend to be talked about rather than projected; and, as a result,
the plays have little theatrical life. In Kyd's play, however, most
of the sensational and bloody action is performed before the eyes
of the audience. The only events narrated in *The Spanish Tragedy*
are those that have occurred before the play begins: the battle,
described in the Senecan manner, and Andrea's descent into the
underworld, which is adapted from the sixth book of Virgil's
Aeneid. Indeed, Kyd is important chiefly because of his genius
for developing the theatrical possibilities of his story—for crowd-
ing the stage with vivid action.

We can see the relation of Kydian to Senecan tragedy by comparing *The Spanish Tragedy* with *Cornelia,* Kyd's own translation
of *Cornelie,* an imitation of Seneca written by the French dramatist Robert Garnier.[5] If we describe the action of *Cornelia* in general terms, we can make it sound very much like *The Spanish
Tragedy.* In the background off the stage is a war, and in the
foreground Cornelia, like Bel-imperia, grieves for two men she
has loved and lost to murderous enemies. Crassus, the first of
these men, was killed in battle; and the second one, Pompey the
Great, was treacherously killed by friends of Julius Caesar. Scipio,
the father of Cornelia, is trying to revenge the death of Pompey.
In Act IV, Caesar's villainy sets in motion an additional revenge

action in the conspiracy of Brutus and Cassius. Cornelia's grief moves her alternately to cry for revenge and to contemplate suicide. Next to Cornelia's, the main voices are those of Cicero and the Chorus. Cicero debates suicide and revenge with Cornelia, urging her to accept the will of heaven. The Chorus concludes each act with a discussion of the powers that govern men: God and the gods, the stars, and Fortune—all have their turns.

In *The Spanish Tragedy,* too, the characters philosophize about God and Fortune, and Hieronimo wavers between suicide and revenge; but in Garnier's play the rhetorical handwringing and philosophizing are all we are given. In *The Spanish Tragedy* there is the exciting intrigue of revenge and counter-revenge; in *Cornelia,* Scipio's revenge is attempted in a battle that is only described; and the conspiracy of Brutus and Cassius is not developed at all within the play. In *The Spanish Tragedy,* the antagonist, Lorenzo, is an active, fascinating character; in *Cornelia,* Caesar appears only once, to be warned by Antony that he has enemies and to philosophize about human destiny.

For the intrigues and for Kyd's cunning and ruthless villain we must look to other sources. True, Seneca's tyrants are ruthless and devious, but there is more madness about them than cunning, and their intrigues are never given any real attention. As Alfred Harbage has pointed out, the greatest innovation of *The Spanish Tragedy* is its combination of Senecan tragedy with the intrigue characteristic of the Roman comedies of Plautus and Terence.[6] This is a striking development, for the new emphasis on clever trickery gives a bizarre and almost comic rather than a tragic tone to much of the action. Elizabethan drama usually mingles the comic and the tragic, but only in this type initiated by Kyd is there often a true union of the two in an esthetic whole having its own distinctive tone and point of view. In the medieval mystery plays there had been comic action to farce out the scenes of biblical history, and so Elizabethan chronicle history plays typically mingled hornpipes and funerals, as Sir Philip Sidney charged of the earlier Elizabethan drama generally. The morality play and its offspring in the political and moral interludes of the sixteenth century were the only pre-Kydian dramatic forms that combined intrigue with serious action to achieve something like his effect.[7]

The Spanish Tragedy, like the moralities, suspends men between a heaven and a hell and then assigns them to one or the other place at the conclusion of the action. The morality's Vice, an agent of Satan, is a cunning villain who uses intrigue to destroy men.[8] But there the resemblance between Kyd and the moralities stops, for the Vice as tempter of mankind is a personified abstraction who is combatted by another personified abstraction, the Good Angel, and so the conflict in a morality is as stiffly allegorical as in Seneca it is stiffly philosophical.

The most important source for the characters and action of *The Spanish Tragedy* is the Elizabethan conception of both Spain and Italy as the devil's workshops. To Reformation Protestants, the Pope seemed a devil; and they thought Machiavelli had given rulers a charter to make the world the devil's kingdom in *The Prince*, which advises the ruler to appeal to men's selfish motives and their fears while appearing to uphold norms of ideal behavior.[9] *The Spanish Tragedy* was written in the decade of the Spanish Armada, when Protestant England was threatened not only by invasion but also by Catholic and Spanish conspiracies against Elizabeth and her rule. And in translations of Continental histories and *novelle* Kyd and his contemporaries could find many lurid tales about such families as the Medici, providing material for their conception of Italy and Spain as countries inhabited by "Machiavels" like Lorenzo, willful and lustful women like Bel-imperia, and unscrupulous *bravi* like Pedringano.[10]

II *Action and Character*

The Spanish Tragedy was a great popular success partly because of contemporary anxiety about Spain, but mostly because of its intrinsic appeal. Kyd brought together the most exciting features of several literary traditions to create a play that exploits the possibilities of the stage more fully than almost any earlier play had done. The sensational theatrical features of the play must have pleased the popular audience the most. The frightening figures of the ghost and Revenge are on the stage throughout, creating a chilling atmosphere as their deadly influence becomes ever more apparent. There are great spectacles of all kinds, from executions to royal banquets. Nine people die on stage, and Kyd has exercised ingenuity in devising a variety of means and circumstances for killing: first, Horatio is plucked from the arms of his love to be hanged and stabbed in his father's arbor; next, Serberine is shot as he waits patiently to learn his master's will

(meantime Alexandro has come within a word or two of the
stake, and Villuppo has been sent off to dire tortures). The most
bizarre of the deaths is that of Pedringano, who laughs his way to
the gallows: certain that he will be turned back at the top of the
ladder by a pardon from his master, he is instead turned *off* the
ladder in a noose when the box that is supposed to contain his
pardon proves to be empty. There have now been two murders
and an execution, so the next death is a suicide. From the bizarre
we pass to the pathetic as old Isabella, desperate in her grief for
Horatio, tears down the arbor and runs a sword through her
bosom. The only remaining possibility for the climax of the play
is the massing of death on death. In the last act Kyd gives us two
murders and a suicide in the play-within-the-play, and he follows
these with Hieronimo's biting out his tongue and then stabbing
the Duke of Castile and himself. Whether staging murders, love
scenes, scenes of tense intrigue, or royal shows, Kyd designs the
action to make full use of the Elizabethan theater. A gallery above
the rear of the stage can be used in many scenes, and the whole
area of the stage is exploited in most scenes because of the presence on-stage of an audience or of people eavesdropping on the
central action.

Motivating the variety of spectacle is the full range of human
emotions, all depicted at extreme moments of passion or madness
and giving way to each other with breathtaking speed. Love that
sweeps up to a sexual climax before our eyes is swiftly followed
by grief that sinks to suicidal despair. A laughing fool is turned
off to his death in a noose. Proud and happy parents applaud the
murder of their children, and then cry out in agony when they discover what has happened. This complex variety and rapid change
of emotions springs directly from the structure of the intrigue,
whose complexity requires that each major character be able to
enter the action in several different ways. For a writer of imagina-
tion, the resulting complexity of the characters will give them a
life of their own, partly freed from those aspects of his control
that are merely manipulative. Complexity of action and structure
thus implies artistic richness, and we find some of this richness in
The Spanish Tragedy, but of course the form Kyd invented did
not reach its full potential until it came into the hands of Shakespeare a few years later.

Although character begins as a product of the action, we can

understand the artful structure of the play best if we examine the
characters before we analyze the evolution of the plot. One of the
virtues of the play is that almost every person who appears on
the stage *has* a character, both in the sense that he is given some
individuality and in the sense that his action is made to spring
from motivation that is clear and psychologically valid. And the
central characters are capable of convincing change in response to
their experience. Even Revenge and the ghost of Andrea are true
dramatic characters. Revenge might be regarded as the author's
scapegoat for his own relish of the show. Again and again we can
feel Revenge's enjoyment of the cruel intrigue and of the process
of initiating Andrea in the mysteries of his bloody rites. Revenge
is patient, smiling, deadly. Beside him is Andrea, at first innocently looking about and wondering, then increasingly caught up
in shifting emotions as Revenge arouses his lust for blood to the
point where finally he is gratified by the suffering and death of
friends as well as foes (IV. v. 1–12). His human, impatient fears
that revenge will fail are adroitly played off against Revenge's
calm, implacable fatality (III. xv. 13–28).

Other characters, too, arrange themselves in balanced and contrasted pairs. The honest and loyal Alexandro is set against the
treacherous and vile Villuppo. The Spanish King, whose compla-
cent self-concern at last deafens him to cries for justice, is contrasted with the Portuguese Viceroy, whose self-concerned feelings of guilt over the supposed death of his son drive him to seek
a scapegoat and so deafen *him* to cries for justice, too. Much more
important is the contrast between Horatio and Balthazar as men
and as lovers. Both are active and masculine in battle, but only
Horatio is also a man of action in love. His courtship of Bel-
imperia is as physically direct as it can well be. He wants to
yield nothing that his manly force has won to men whose only
claim to superiority is their rank.

It is debatable whether Horatio is really more honorable than
Balthazar, but he knows how to make himself seem so in order to
get his way with Bel-imperia. Although Horatio's speech is
courtly, it is natural and easy compared with that of Balthazar,[11] whose consistent artificiality in speech and behavior suggests that he is governed by conventions. First Balthazar attempts
to woo Bel-imperia by means of the conventional rhetoric of Petrarchan love poetry, speaking of his "servitude" to her and saying

that his heart is lodged in her bosom and that she is "beauty's bower" (I. iv. 77–99). When this kind of rhetoric has failed him, his conflicting emotions of hope and despair result in an even more artificial rhetorical style (II. i. 19–30). Balthazar, a weak man in any arena where his skill as a warrior is without value, is helpless in the power of his love; and, if it were left to him, he would simply retire from the field in confusion. His weakness becomes despicable when he surrenders command of himself to Lorenzo and his plan to murder Horatio.

Balthazar thus starts out as a lover victimized by a too-great passion which strips him of the ability to think or act for himself. In this stage of his development he is bested by his enemy, Horatio. Then Balthazar is mastered by his "friend," Lorenzo, who makes his love produce an act of hate. This double defeat of Balthazar has been suggested symbolically in his analogous defeat in battle, when he surrendered to both Lorenzo and Horatio (I. ii. 152–65).

Lorenzo is more complicated than either Balthazar or Horatio. In the passage just referred to, he is contrasted with Horatio, but usually he is set off against Balthazar, Hieronimo, and Belimperia. His friendship masks the desire to master or destroy others. Like Revenge, he enjoys his own cunning and feels neither love nor pity. Using his "friendship" for Balthazar to rationalize his actions, he gives full sway to a terrifying egoism that enjoys making puppets of other people as an end in itself. In contrast with Balthazar, he at first seems clear-headed and resourceful, without any passion of the sort that makes his friend vulnerable. But self-loving megalomania is as dangerous a passion as love of a woman. Lorenzo is destroyed because he cannot resist his own clever plotting when it occurs to him that Serberine and Pedringano, accomplices in the murder of Horatio, might betray him to Hieronimo. Self-concerned fear and egotistical enjoyment of making puppets of others push Lorenzo to kill them both. Ironically enough, only because of their deaths does Hieronimo learn of Lorenzo's guilt.

In his self-destroying attempt at self-preservation Lorenzo may remind us of Pedringano, who plays a crucial part in the action of the play and who also epitomizes in grotesque fashion many of the follies of humanity that take more serious forms in some of the other characters. Pedringano seeks security and happiness in an unscrupulous and selfish "service" to another. He exemplifies man's perverse faith in the security that worldly riches and power seem to guarantee. His silly rationalizations of villainy are pathetically human as well as absurd, and the grotesquerie of his behavior on the gallows is one of the finest fusions of the pathetic and the absurd in all the Elizabethan drama. He is really a puppet already dangling on the cord Lorenzo has prepared, but he is assured of his pardon and so enjoys himself at the expense of the hangman, priding himself in his wit and his "superior" position, blissfully secure in his certainty that justice is a joke and that crime is only a word when compared with what he takes to be the realities of life.

Bel-imperia is a true sister to Lorenzo.[12] Her "imperious" will is a match for his, and she serves herself in her passion for love as he serves himself in his passion for domination. Lorenzo's friendship for Balthazar is made the tool of an ulterior motive, and her love for Horatio is a means for the revenge of Andrea, if also an end in itself. Like her brother, Bel-imperia is fearful; but in her case this emotion is part of her womanly character when she is about to consummate her love for Horatio. Usually she is braver than Lorenzo; and, in the one scene in which they openly clash, she turns her wit and her scorn upon him and triumphs over him (III. x.). In her imperious nature, love and hate, fire and ice surely belong together, as do boldness and timidity.

Hieronimo is the one character on whom all the others impinge either directly in the action or indirectly through parallels like the one that relates him to the Portuguese Viceroy as a stricken father seeking revenge. He is the one truly changing character in the play. At first we are shown that he is a judicious and loyal subject and a proud father. In the second scene there is a moment of conflict between these loyalties when Horatio is a rival of Lorenzo, who is the King's nephew, over the capture of Balthazar. This clash foreshadows Lorenzo's murder of Horatio, with the consequent dilemma for Hieronimo on which the tragedy concentrates its psychological and philosophical interest. Although Hieronimo is a judge, the King's justice fails him in his need. He stands cruelly divided between a maddening grief that cries for blood and a lifelong devotion to caution, reason, and orderly process. His dilemma cuts him off from all other people, and we typically find him alone and in agony at the start of his scenes. As Wolfgang Clemen has said, Hieronimo is the first important character in Elizabethan drama to be created mainly through soliloquies.[13]

Hieronimo's response to his son's murder differs from his wife's in one crucial respect. She, too, is made desperate with grief; but, whereas he has the quest for justice to focus his mind on, she can only turn inward in her grief, and her mind crumbles in suicidal madness. Hieronimo's mind breaks for a time, too, especially in the scene with the old man whose son has been murdered. The shock of recognizing himself in this man shatters Hieronimo, and perhaps we are to feel that through the remaining action he holds himself together only by a great effort. We can feel his intense nervous strain in scenes of plotting that require him to suppress his emotions (e.g., III. xiv. 118–69). He finally lets all his agony and hatred pour out in his long tirade after the revenges of the play-within-the-play, and in the bloody excesses of the catastrophe we witness his collapse as a rational being.

III   *Tragic Action and Comic Plot*

Peter W. Biesterfeldt has written of *The Spanish Tragedy* that it has the structure neither of the crisis plot of classical tragedy nor the *ab ovo* plot of English chronicle plays.[14] With a crisis plot, the play would begin only after the murder of Horatio and would omit the intrigues of Act III, leaping directly from Hieronimo's discovery of his son's body to his crisis when the King is deaf to his pleas for justice (III. xii and xiii). With an *ab ovo* plot the story would be told "from the egg," beginning with the death of Andrea, or with his romance with Bel-imperia, or perhaps even with his birth. As Alfred Harbage has suggested, the structure of the play does not really derive from the tragic form at all, but from the form of Roman comedy, especially Terence, whose plays were subjected to analysis by every English schoolboy. Renaissance writers and literary critics turned to Roman drama for models and to Roman criticism for precepts.[15] The most specific statements on dramatic structure were those of Horace in his *Ars Poetica* and of Aelius Donatus in his fourth-century commentary on Terence. Donatus' analysis was studied along with the plays, and his statements on the act-division of comedy were combined with those of Horace on tragedy to form the basis for Renaissance efforts to lay down the precepts for the structure of tragedy as well as of comedy.

In 1482 the Florentine scholar Christopher Landino published
an edition of Horace offering an explanation of act-structure
based on Donatus. Landino's analysis was to be the nucleus of
the growing Renaissance theory that reached its final form with
the writings of Julius Caesar Scaliger in the sixteenth century.
Landino writes: "But it must be especially avoided lest the fable
contain more or less than five acts. For the matter is so divided
into five that the first part unfolds the argument. The second
seeks to bring to an end the things which already have been begun. The third brings on the perturbation and the impediments
and despair of the desired thing. The fourth brings a remedy for
the impending evil. The fifth brings the whole to the desired outcome." [16]

Landino prescribes five acts, but he is really describing a way
of developing an action, regardless of where act-divisions fall. Although *The Spanish Tragedy* has only four acts, its structure follows Landino, for Kyd's Act III does the work of Landino's third
and fourth acts. Kyd's third act is about twice as long as any
other act, and it contains two clearly distinguishable plot units. [17]
It is, therefore, no distortion of Kyd's structure to think of Act III
as a sort of double act, and we may speak of the action as being
divided into five parts: Acts I, II, III. i–vii, III. viii–xv, and IV.

Act I begins the exposition that "unfolds the argument." In it,
we meet all the major characters and learn of the conflicts out of
which the action is to grow. The Spaniard Don Andrea, lover of
Bel-imperia, has been killed in a war between Spain and Portugal
by Balthazar, the son of the Portuguese Viceroy. From the underworld Andrea's ghost has been sent back to earth with Revenge to
witness retribution against Balthazar. The induction of Revenge
and Andrea introduces the themes of love and hate, justice and
revenge. The first consequence of the death of Andrea has been
the capture of Balthazar by the avenging Horatio. This capture
leads to Balthazar's confinement in the court of Spain, where he
meets Bel-imperia and again becomes embattled with Horatio,
this time as a rival in love. Horatio is accepted as Bel-imperia's
lover because he has been Andrea's friend and because she wants
revenge for Andrea's death. The motives of revenge and love have
thus moved from their origin in Andrea and Revenge into the action of the play proper, for Horatio is clearly a second Andrea in
his two roles as lover of Bel-imperia and enemy of Balthazar and

Lorenzo. There is thus an organic connection between the induction and the play.

The Spanish Tragedy follows the structure of the most complex Roman comedies in having two important parallel plots: in Act I, the Portuguese Viceroy's cries for revenge against the supposed murderer of his son foreshadow the actions of Hieronimo in the main plot, actions that are as yet only latent in the "unfolding of the argument" in Act I. The action in the Portuguese court is also important as it completes the picture of the change from war to peace, a change in the relations of Spain and Portugal that provides a framework for the action concerning Hieronimo.

Act II "seeks to bring to an end the things which already have been begun." Horatio and Bel-imperia meet to enjoy their love, and Horatio is murdered by Balthazar and Lorenzo because of this love. The act closes upon Hieronimo's grief and his determination to avenge his son, which starts the complication of the plot that is developed in Act III. The sequence of Horatio's death and his father's reaction is the "heart scene" of the play. All the previous action leads up to this moment as a catastrophe, and all the action that comes after flows from it as a new beginning. In the placing of the heart scene, Kyd parallels Terence, in whom it usually comes at the end of Act II or the beginning of Act III.[18]

The murder of Horatio concludes the conflict among the young warriors and lovers, and it also concludes the second phase of the framework action, which is joining with the main action: in Act I, peace came to Spain and Portugal; in Act II, the rulers have decided to seal that peace with the marriage of Balthazar and Bel-imperia, and the Duke of Castile has been asked to be sure that his daughter cooperates. The murder of Horatio seems to the perverse Lorenzo to bring to an end the action necessary to win her for Balthazar.

The scene of Horatio's death likewise clearly *initiates* all the action that follows, both the efforts of Lorenzo to hide the traces of his crime and those of Hieronimo to find out who murdered his son and to see that the guilty are punished. The chorus at the end of Act II suggests the structural function of the act. To Andrea all seems ended and lost, but Revenge knows that only the exposition is now completed, that the real complications of the action are to follow and will be consummated in the wished-for death of Balthazar (II. vi. 1–11).

Act III is the complication of the play, combining the functions of Acts III and IV in Landino's analysis of the five-act structure: "The third brings on the perturbation and the impediments and despair of the desired thing. The fourth brings a remedy for the impending evil." The "desired thing" is, of course, Hieronimo's revenge for Horatio. The plot action in the first half of Act III develops Lorenzo's attempts to prevent this desired thing by destroying his accomplices Pedringano and Serberine. The plot action of the second half of the act contains Hieronimo's discovery of Lorenzo's guilt and his futile efforts to obtain justice. Hieronimo's choice between suicide and the quest for justice and between inaction and revenge in scenes xii–xiii is the "crisis" of the play, the last moment of doubt before the action turns decisively toward a catastrophe that will make Revenge very happy.

The heart scene and the crisis are the structural pillars of the play, its scenes of *necessary* action for the working out of the story Kyd has conceived. Had Hieronimo come upon his son's body a few seconds sooner than he did, he would have seen the murderers, and the crisis could have followed almost immediately. But much would have been lost. Kyd has used the intervening scenes to develop important aspects of Hieronimo's dilemma and his character. His quest for justice is made to include a quest for knowledge, and the combination of these two quests broadens the scope of the play by making Hieronimo ask about the relation of appearance to reality and about the nature of reality itself (III. ii. 1–23). We are made to see how Hieronimo's desire to punish thwarts his desire to know: his obsessive will to destroy Pedringano for one murder keeps him from trying to find out whether that murder might provide clues to the case he is personally interested in.

It is essential to observe that there is much more to these intrigue scenes than the mere forwarding of the plot. In the analysis of a play, it is necessary to avoid a critical perspective that focuses on plot and may see the complications of the Pedringano story as mere inflation of the action. Even in plot analysis we must always be aware that a deeper study of the play will seek an inner action that is beneath the surface of the plot and is closely related to theme and meaning.[19] For example, part of the frustration of the "desired thing" in Act III is its first scene, which is laid in the Portuguese court and has nothing to do with Hieronimo. As part of a parallel plot, it is unified with the main plot at the level of its parallel inner action and theme of revenge. At this level of relationship it demonstrates the need for caution in situations like Hieronimo's in the next scene, a need that the plot involving Hieronimo has not developed up to this moment.[20] The main plot and the subplot thus combine as a single action, and each must always be considered in relation to the other.

In Kyd's artful construction of the action, the third movement passes directly into the fourth, for Lorenzo's efforts to frustrate the "desired thing" ironically disclose the "remedy" Hieronimo has sought when Pedringano's letter to Lorenzo is taken to Hieronimo by the Hangman. Lorenzo thinks he has solved his problem and made himself secure by killing Serberine and Pedringano, but he could not be more mistaken. Hieronimo has perhaps hoped that he could solve his chief problem if he knew who killed Horatio, but he now finds that such hopes could not have been more futile, and his major crisis is upon him: Should he kill himself or go to the King? And, when he cannot speak to the King, should he seek revenge? He decides on revenge, and Act III concludes with a scene that draws together all the lines of action in preparation for the catastrophe. Thinking that Balthazar is to win Belimperia, Lorenzo ends his plots and makes peace with Hieronimo, who has already decided to smile upon his enemies until he kills them. The rulers of Spain and Portugal set their hopes on the wedding of Balthazar and Bel-imperia, and Hieronimo plans to use this royal occasion for his revenge.

The fifth movement of the play, Act IV, "brings the *whole* to the desired outcome" in the catastrophe that joins the revenge action with the action between Spain and Portugal in the play-within-the-play. This playlet seems to celebrate a royal wedding by staging a pretended action, but it only pretends to be a pretended action, for the murders are real and the celebration turns out to be based on an illusion. I shall discuss this complicated matter at greater length in the chapters that follow; but, from what I have just said, it is clear that the catastrophe in the playlet not only unites the frame and the inner actions but implies a close relation between the various levels of pretended and "real" action and actors, between the actors and the three audiences who watch the play-within-the-play: the Spanish and Portuguese royalty, Revenge and Andrea, and the paying audience in the theater.[21]

IV *Scene Construction*

Kyd is no less skillful in the construction of individual scenes
than he is in the design of the play as a whole. The third scene of
the play may be analyzed as a typical example because it is part
of the microcosmic two-scene subplot that epitomizes nearly every structural and thematic element of the play. This scene, like
most of the others, is constructed artfully to have variety in its
modes of dramatic expression, dynamic development in its unfolding conflict, and a balanced contrast between opposed characters
who generate the conflict. In its action it is especially typical of
the scenes near it in the main plot, scenes in which two rival
forces contend against each other and a third force adjudicates
the conflict. In the other scenes the dramatic focus is not only on
the judge but also on the rivals or the nature of the rivalry; here,
however, the focus is almost entirely on the judge and the way
his judgment may be clouded if he is emotionally involved in the
rivalry. This gives the scene great importance in relation to later
scenes of the play in which Hieronimo is a judge in passion.

The scene begins with an expository dialogue of four lines between the Viceroy and Alexandro that tells us the Portuguese
have acknowledged their defeat in the late war by sending tribute
to the Spanish King. The fact that Alexandro speaks like a loyal
courtier will be important later in the scene when Villuppo accuses him of treason and murder. After this opening series of four
one-line speeches the Viceroy has a thirty-eight-line monologue
in which he pours forth his sorrows. He does not merely speak,
however. The long monologue is made more dramatic by his
throwing himself from the throne to the ground in the midst of
his lamentations and then holding out his crown for Fortune to
take from him. The speech moves from emotion to emotion as
self-pity and a suppressed sense of guilt struggle for dominance.
The first ten lines express a self-pitying sorrow, but do no more
than hint at an analysis of the emotion and its causes. The chief
interest is in the expression of emotion in words and actions of
self-abasement before the court.[22] In the next eighteen lines the
Viceroy's self-pity impels him to find someone to blame in the person of the goddess of Fortune, whose unjust treatment of such
worthy men as himself is analyzed in some detail. Emotion has
found an object and, consequently, lessens its intensity as rationalization competes with it.

The rhetorical pattern of the Viceroy's speech becomes more formal as his wild grief gives way to rationalizing restraint. Rationalization in turn gives way to true thought once he realizes that if blind Fortune is responsible for his state, then his lamentations can in no way help his condition except by giving relief to his feelings, and in the last ten lines of the monologue he probes more deeply into the relation between his situation and his emotion. The rhetoric now stresses logical sequences of thought as he comes to see that his own ambition, not Fortune, has caused the loss of his army and, he supposes, the death of his son Balthazar. His conclusion is that he should have gone to war himself and left Balthazar at home, but in looking back over his long speech we must particularly note how grief and self-pity have made it difficult for him to face his own guilt, easy for him to shift the blame to Fortune.

The passage that follows the Viceroy's monologue contrasts with it in form by the use of stichomythia[23] to express the seesaw nature of the conflict between reason and passion for control of the Viceroy. First, Alexandro tries to reason the Viceroy out of his guilty fear that Balthazar is dead, but the Viceroy will not listen. Villuppo shows that he has a fine grasp of the psychology of the situation as he intervenes to confirm the Viceroy's fear and at the same time give him someone outside himself to blame for his defeat and the loss of his son. As we have seen, the Viceroy's "ear is ready to receive ill news," and Villuppo plays directly to that readiness (I. iii. 56).

Villuppo charges that Alexandro treacherously killed Balthazar in the crisis of the battle, and that this crime was the sole cause of the Portuguese defeat. The Viceroy need no longer blame himself for anything. Alexandro can reply that Villuppo's story is a lie, but the Viceroy's self-pity and guilt have destroyed his ability to judge fairly. All his passionate grief is immediately transformed into wrath, and he will not even listen to Alexandro. Instead, he projects onto him the fault he had earlier admitted in himself—ambition leading to breach of faith (ll. 33 and 85, 34 and 77). Earlier he took his crown off to offer it to Fortune; now he takes it off and puts it on again as a sign of the certainty of his authority and his "justice." The irony of his failure to see how he has been fooled is reinforced if we remember that, just before Villuppo offered his story, the Viceroy said the Spanish had probably murdered Balthazar after capturing him: "They reck no laws that meditate revenge" (48). This line gives sententious expression to the main thematic import of the scene: its demonstration of the injustice that revenge may cause in the name of justice.

The construction of this scene may be summarized quite simply. Our attention is directed to the conflicting emotions and thoughts of the person on whom the scene will focus. His internal dramatic conflict is then projected into an external conflict. The external conflict arises out of and then transforms the internal conflict, so that a dramatic change takes place both within and between characters. At the start, the Viceroy seems close to Alexandro; at the finish, his new mental state is expressed in action as Alexandro is sent off under guard. The seesaw of stichomythia comes at the dramatic center of the scene, its turning point; and it balances the earlier monologue of inner conflict against the later alternation of fairly long set speeches with shorter speeches in a dialogue of bitter dramatic conflict.

The structure of this scene is like that of several of the scenes which begin with long speeches by Hieronimo, the other grieving father, and then go on to develop action growing out of and altering his state of mind. But, above all, the structure of the scene is important as it demonstrates general truths about Kyd's methods of construction, whether studied in a single scene or in the whole play. Inner action is relentlessly given dramatic expression in elaborate verbal and theatrical forms.[24] Deep feeling is rarely uttered in compressed phrases that seem simple but that yield subtle complexities as we ponder them: simile, not metaphor, is the rule as emotion is developed at length, usually in elaborate rhetorical poetry. Rhetorical speeches and sensational theatrical action are brought together in patterns of parallel and contrast to construct scenes; and these individual scenes are fitted together in an elaborate combination of patterns, both of cause and effect and of parallel and contrast, to make up the plot of the play as a whole.

Kyd's great skill at providing theatrical expression for the inner action of his drama makes *The Spanish Tragedy* a brilliant stage play, but the question remains whether so sensationally theatrical a work can transcend the melodramatic to become tragic. Theatrical or not, what happens when a tragic action is clothed in a plot of comic design? Can the play be taken seriously as a work having deep implications about the human condition, or is it only important as a model to be developed by better artists, being in itself a fair target for parody? In order to answer these questions, we must study the play in greater detail and with special attention to the possibility that its elaborate rhetorical and theatrical form and development of themes are themselves an expression of its tragic meaning.

CHAPTER 2

The Theme and Structure
of The Spanish Tragedy

I   *Structure as Theme*

WHAT kind of play is *The Spanish Tragedy?* If we say that it is a work of theatrical genius, sensational and melodramatic in its manipulation of externals, do we deny it all possibility of having tragic depth and internal power? We may note at the outset that, whatever the limitations of Kyd's dramatic technique, his insistence on having his themes arise from characters in action on the stage is in one way, at least, an advance over Senecan tragedy, in which too often there is a great deal of "philosophy" that needs the test of characters in action. Moreover, Kyd has manipulated his "external" theatrical elements to create complex patterns of action, character, and language that have complex and profound implications even though they are made up of simple units; and the audience must perceive these patterns in order to understand the play.

For example, the play depends for both effect and meaning on parallels and contrasts between its different lines of action. Hieronimo's mistrust of Bel-imperia's letter accusing Lorenzo and Balthazar of the murder of Horatio is only developed superficially in psychological terms, and we in the audience accept his mistrust chiefly because, in the preceding scene, in parallel circumstances having nothing to do with Hieronimo, *we* have seen that such accusations can be false (III. i–ii). Kyd has thus sought to achieve the effect he desires by manipulating the audience as well as the characters of his play.[1] The characters tend to speak as much to the audience as to one another;[2] and the reason may be that Kyd means to exploit the arts of language not only to develop character and action but also to persuade and affect the audience so that it will be more immediately involved with his play than is usual.

Indeed, *The Spanish Tragedy* goes beyond Hamlet's assertion that a play is an image of reality to suggest that the play world *is* the real world or its symbolic equivalent. Perhaps the most striking feature of this play, as of *Hamlet,* is the play-within-the-play; but, whereas in *Hamlet* the playlet is only a pretended re-enactment of a murder, the playlet in *The Spanish Tragedy* is also a *vehicle* for murders. At its conclusion, Hieronimo tells his audience that it was mistaken to think it had watched "fabulously counterfeit" action, for the murders have been "perform'd" in two senses (IV. iv. 77, 129). From *Hamlet* we may infer that, if the play-within-the-play is a mirror of the *Hamlet* world, perhaps the *Hamlet* world is likewise a mirror of our world. When the royal audience for Hieronimo's play sees that the play world is a real part of Spain, we may suddenly see that events in Spain are part of our world, that the characters have been made to work on our emotions because Kyd wants us to feel their passions directly, and not only as part of an esthetic whole from which we maintain a large degree of detachment. We are to see the characters in Kyd's play as people whom we might almost accept as part of our world at the same time that we recognize the artifice that has created them and know that we are at a higher level of awareness because we are in an audience.

The idea of an intimate relation between those in the play and those outside it is implicit in the use Kyd makes of Andrea and Revenge. Andrea has precipitated the action he now watches as an audience, and Revenge both directs and witnesses the working out of the plot. Andrea even seems to enter the action of the play in the person of Horatio who, like Andrea, becomes the clandestine lover of Bel-imperia, is killed by Balthazar and his cohorts, and so causes a bloody revenge. It is no coincidence that revenge for Andrea is accomplished through revenge for Horatio in a play-within-the-play: just as the playlet contains murders for revenge of Horatio, with Hieronimo both "author and actor in this tragedy," so the whole play is an enactment of murders for revenge of Andrea who, if not its author, is its inspiration and a key participant both in spirit and in the person of Horatio (IV. iv. 147).

The relation between the playlet and the play has still more implications than these. When Hieronimo says he is the author as well as an actor in his tragic playlet, he is claiming that he controls his own fate. He is not aware that above the level of his will and his authorship of action is another author, Revenge, who is using him for his own ends (or that above Revenge may be other authors like Pluto and Proserpina or Thomas Kyd; this last author is of course using everyone on the stage and in the audience for his own ends). Through this pattern we can see that the question the play asks is the one that all tragedies ask in one way or another: What are the forces that govern human destiny? Can men govern their own actions, joining the powers of author and actor to exercise complete freedom of will? Or is the freedom of the will only partial, so that man is less an author than an actor governed by a script created by his previous actions, by the passions of his character, and by the powers of heaven and hell, of chance and circumstance? [3]

Kyd invites us, as Revenge invites Andrea, to "imagine thou/ What 'tis to be subject to destiny" (III. xv. 27–28) and to sit down and "see the mystery" of tragic fate (I. i. 90). Of course the mystery of man's fate is, in part, what makes it tragic. If we knew the whole truth about our situation, we could use our reason to act in accordance with that truth; but, as it is, we do not know whether we live in an absurd universe having no order and no justice, whether we can author our own fates, or whether we are governed by powers whose wills we can only guess and may fulfill only unconsciously and ironically, against our own wills.

Repeatedly, the play gives us scenes of men who are unable to understand the powers above them. The most ingenious of these is the scene in Act III when Pedringano kills Serberine and is arrested by the Watch. Pedringano and Serberine were Lorenzo's accomplices in the murder of Horatio, and Lorenzo fears that they will betray him to Hieronimo. He decides, therefore, to destroy them. Serberine is told to go to the park behind the palace at eight o'clock; Pedringano is sent there to kill him; and the Watch is also told to be there. And not one of the men knows why he has really been sent to the park. Serberine's awareness is the least of all; he has no idea why he has been sent for, although he is instinctively afraid of the forces that may look down on him in the dark (III. iii. 23–27). Pedringano knows that he is to kill Serberine, but does not suspect that this act is to result in his own death. Like Serberine, he is afraid, but he appeals to the goddess Fortune and places his faith in Lorenzo's rewards and promises. The men of the Watch know only that they have been commanded to guard where they have never been sent before, and they do not dream that they are the key part of a pattern of crime and retribution prearranged by Lorenzo.

In fact, no one comprehends the pattern in its entirety. Serberine sees nothing but the command of his master. Pedringano sees Serberine and his reward, but he does not see the Watch or the real plan of Lorenzo. The Watch see Serberine and Pedringano, and they know the power of the rulers, but they do not see how that power is being used in this case. Lorenzo is not on stage, but we must imagine him exulting as the clever stage manager who has masterminded the scene. But even Lorenzo does not see the final level of control: the persons of Revenge and Andrea, who have really arranged this pattern of crime and retribution, and have arranged it chiefly to destroy Lorenzo and Balthazar. There is no evidence that either Serberine or Pedringano would ever have willingly betrayed Lorenzo; but, after his arrest, Pedringano writes to Lorenzo reminding him of his crimes and begging his master to save him as he had promised to do. When Pedringano has been hanged, the executioner finds this letter and takes it to Hieronimo. Thus, although Lorenzo thinks he is the master of fate, the very means he employs to save himself are his ruin. His unreasonably fearful self-love has betrayed him to Revenge, an unseen power that destroys men by preying upon such passions through a pattern that is in every way ironic, as we shall see.

The central image of man in *The Spanish Tragedy* is thus a figure standing alone in semi-darkness, able to see and apparently able to control those below him in the hierarchy of power, although without understanding them, but often unable even to *see* those above him. If men could see those above themselves, they might realize that they are manipulated in the same way that they manipulate others; and they might then learn to treat other men more humanely. Humans destroy each other and are destroyed in turn because they do not understand that they are related to others not as superior to inferior, not as person to object or other, but as images of each other, or, most deeply of all, as forms of each other. If Lorenzo could see Revenge destroy him as he destroys Pedringano, he might know that what he does to Pedringano he really does to himself.

Hieronimo may progress toward a blind and isolated egotism like Lorenzo's, in which he thinks he is both author and actor of fate and does not rightly look above himself, but for most of the play he is desperately aware of the need to see:

O eyes, no eyes, but fountains fraught with tears;
O life, no life, but lively form of death;

O world, no world, but mass of public wrongs,
Confus'd and fill'd with murder and misdeeds;
O sacred heavens! if this unhallow'd deed,
If this inhuman and barbarous attempt,
If this incomparable murder thus
Of mine, but now no more my son,
Shall unreveal'd and unrevenged pass,
How should we term your dealings to be just,
If you unjustly deal with those that in your justice trust? (III.ii.1–11)

This speech is in many ways a key to the themes and structure of
the play. Hieronimo, alone on the stage, is crying out to the unseen powers of heaven and hell, asking the questions that tragic
action raises: Is there any order in the world? Are the heavens
just? At the end of the speech, a letter falls at his feet that accuses Lorenzo and Balthazar of the murder of Horatio; but Hieronimo suspects the letter, and his loneliness, doubts, and fears are
not allayed. The fearsome isolation of the tragic individual is expressed in every word he utters. Hieronimo is blinded by the tears
of his passionate grief, and in his blindness he leaves unclear or
else denies the true relations of things, even their very identities:
"eyes, no eyes." If Hieronimo were not blinded by tears, he might
be able to see Andrea and Revenge who are sitting right in front
of him with an answer to his question. His inability to see them
gives his speech a level of meaning of which he is not aware,
again implying a failure to perceive identities and relations. He
says "O life, no life, but lively form of death," meaning that his
life is a painful living death; but the ghost of Andrea is another
"lively form of death," almost an alternate form of Hieronimo, like
him writhing in agony for revenge.

Although Hieronimo cannot see the parallel or identity of his
level of action with the one above him, these ironies make *us* feel
the relations of the two. In another way, also, the speech makes us
feel that the parts of reality are related by parallels and identities
of structure. The rhetoric itself, as so often in the play, implies
that such a pattern underlies reality, that it is necessary to perceive parallels as well as patterns of cause and effect in viewing
the ascending planes of reality. Since there are no logical connec-
tives between the major units of the speech, its logic is entirely
expressed through the implicit relations of its parts:

> O eyes, no eyes, but . . .
> O life, no life, but . . .
> O world, no world, but . . .
> . . . .
> O sacred heavens [implied: no sacred heavens, if there is no
>   justice.] . . .

We must grasp the logic of this structure of parallels in much the same way that we grasp the logic of the parallels between the induction of the ghost and Revenge, the play, and the play-within-the-play; between Serberine, Pedringano, Lorenzo, and Revenge; or between the story of Alexandro and Villuppo and that of Hieronimo. The speech builds upon the traditional parallels or correspondences between the various levels of reality. "Eyes" epitomize in microcosm the problem that "life" also develops. The individual "life" is a microcosm of the life of the body politic or the "world," and the order of the world should conform to the order of the cosmos, governed by "heavens." These significant parallels stress the point that Hieronimo, believing the proper relation of life, world, and heavens to have been destroyed, is tempted to deny their very identities. "Eyes, no eyes"—perhaps we are to see that his emotions blind him not only to Andrea and Revenge but to whatever order and hope of justice there might be in his world, and to the truth contained in the letter that drops at his feet in response to his plea for help.

It may be that there is an important denial of relationship and identity in Hieronimo's statement that Horatio is "now no more my son" (III. ii. 8). He means only to say that Horatio is dead, but perhaps Kyd also means to imply that for Hieronimo his son's death has in some sense ended or transformed their relationship. The two lines of his speech just after he discovers Horatio's body are much like the denials of the "Eyes, no eyes" speech: "Alas, it is Horatio my sweet son!/O no, but he that whilom was my son" (II. v. 14–15). This could give a clue to one of the most puzzling of the mysteries of human destiny the play is concerned with: How are love and hatred related to each other?

One might blindly think of love and hate as unrelated opposites, but they are related in many ways in *The Spanish Tragedy* and in life. Hieronimo loved his son Horatio. But now Horatio has been murdered, and for Hieronimo the positive relationship

to his son is ended. Love for his son is now to be expressed nega-
tively in hatred of the murderers. From this ironic reversal of
emotion the motive of revenge arises. Yet, at a different level, the
motive for revenge arises out of the complete irreconcilability of
love and hate. Don Andrea loves Bel-imperia, and for love of her
goes off to war, an expression of hate. There he is killed, and,
when his soul comes before Minos, Aeacus, and Rhadamanth, the
judges in Hades, Minos describes his fate:

> "This knight," quoth he, "both liv'd and died in love,
> And for his love tried fortune of the wars,
> And by war's fortune lost both love and life."
> "Why then," said Aeacus, "convey him hence,
> To walk with lovers in our fields of love, . . ."
> "No, no," said Rhadamanth, "it were not well
> With loving souls to place a martialist,
> He died in war, and must to martial fields, . . ."
> Then Minos, mildest censor of the three,
> Made this device to end the difference.
> "Send him," quoth he, "to our infernal king,
> To doom him as best seems his majesty." (I.i.38–42, 45–47, 50–53)

The *judges* are thus frustrated, and Andrea is sent to Pluto's palace, where Proserpina turns him over to Revenge. The revenger,
like the chivalric warrior, is a role that combines the lover
and the killer into one: "Awake, Revenge, if love, as love hath
had,/Have yet the power or prevalence in hell!" (III. xv. 13–14).
Revenge thus comes into play when ordinary justice is impossible
because a man has committed acts of violence for love. And revenge fatefully repeats this ironic pattern of motivation, yielding
a series of murders for love. We will discuss the relation of justice and revenge more fully in a few pages, but let us observe
here that the solution Revenge provides for Andrea's problem is
hardly equitable: in order to destroy Balthazar, he will add murder to murder, finally killing no fewer than nine people, of whom
none but Balthazar is one of the Portuguese who had anything to
do with the death of Andrea.

We find love and hate linked together in every part of the
play's chain of motivation. The love of Bel-imperia for Andrea
dies with him, but it inspires both her hatred of his slayer and
her love for Horatio, who, as a friend, also loved Andrea. Bel-

imperia clearly perverts love when she says she will use Horatio's
love to further her revenge for Andrea (I. iv. 60–68). Since it is
partly a shared hatred of Andrea's slayer that brings Bel-imperia
and Horatio together as lovers, it is quite appropriate that they
should talk of love in the language of war, speaking of it paradoxi-
cally as "our warring peace, or peaceful war" (II. ii. 38). When
they meet to make love, this loving sex-war reaches its ironic
catastrophe in the Elizabethan pun that joins the killer and the
lover, the symbolic use of "die" for the sexual climax (II. iv. 47–
48). At the very moment of sexual "death" the lovers are torn
apart and Horatio literally dies at the hands of the jealous and
vengeful Balthazar and Lorenzo. Balthazar, a study in the way
unrequited love can make a person kill for jealousy, knows that
this murder will frustrate his love for Bel-imperia, but he cannot
help himself. He is caught between erotic love and a self-loving
hatred of his rival in which one of them must die: "she'll fly me if
I take revenge./Yet must I take revenge or die myself,/For love
resisted grows impatient" (II. i. 115–17).

The murder of Horatio is, then, brought on by tangled motives
of self-loving hatred and erotic love, but in the murders that follow, the fearful self-love of Lorenzo is pitted chiefly against the
frustrated and sometimes self-pitying paternal love of Hieronimo
that joins with the frustrated erotic love of Bel-imperia to destroy
Balthazar and Lorenzo in the play-within-the-play. This playlet
is a microcosm of the whole play in its motive forces of hate, love,
and egotism:

> BAL. Ah Bashaw, here is love between Erasto
> And fair Perseda, sovereign of my soul.
> HIER. Remove Erasto, mighty Soliman,
> And then Perseda will be quickly won.
> BAL. Erasto is my friend, and while he lives
> Perseda never will remove her love.
> HIER. Let not Erasto live to grieve great Soliman.
> BAL. Dear is Erasto in our princely eye.
> HIER. But if he be your rival, let him die.
> BAL. Why, let him die, so love commandeth me. (IV.iv.39–48)

Love commands a man to kill: this epitomizing line is echoed by
Hieronimo speaking in his own person a little later when he reveals the corpse of Horatio: "The cause was love, whence grew

this mortal hate,/The hate, Lorenzo and young Balthazar,/The love, my son to Bel-imperia" (IV. iv. 98–100).

At times the play seems to suggest that men who lose their love may be so blinded by passion that they seek a perverse satisfaction in killing as a substitute for loving. Lorenzo is capable only of this perverse satisfaction, and Balthazar is driven to it in his frustration. Hieronimo describes thus his expectation of revenge: "Then will I joy amidst my discontent,/Till then my sorrow never shall be spent" (II. v. 55–56). This emotional transformation can even be seen in Andrea. At the outset, he does not seem to care about revenge; at the end of Act II, he wants only his enemies to suffer and laments that Horatio and Bel-imperia have been hurt; but in the final chorus he exults in all the killings as the fulfillment of his desires (IV. v. 1–12).

The imagery of the transformation of Andrea is the basis for the transformations of the characters who dramatize the action caused by the relationship of Andrea and Revenge. As frustrated love changes the heart and soul of a man, he goes on a pilgrimage along strange pathways in the underworld of his spirit. Andrea, who craves a passage for his wandering ghost, finds it only with Revenge. Hieronimo tries to avoid this evil conductor, grieving that men should destroy their souls by their perversions of spiritual values:

> O monstrous times, where murder's set so light,
> And where the soul, that should be shrin'd in heaven,
> Solely delights in interdicted things,
> Still wand'ring in the thorny passages
> That intercepts itself of happiness. (III.vi.90–94)

Balthazar describes his pursuit of Bel-imperia in terms of an erring or wandering pilgrimage:

> Led by the loadstar of her heavenly looks,
> Wends poor oppressed Balthazar,
> As o'er the mountains walks the wanderer,
> Incertain to effect his pilgrimage. (III.x.106–9)

A moment after Balthazar says these words, three men ask Hieronimo what path to take to find Lorenzo. Hieronimo's reply describes the psychology of Lorenzo's response to guilt as a journey, but the description is also colored strongly by Hieronimo's own journey of despair as a result of Lorenzo's crimes:

> There is a path upon your left-hand side,
> That leadeth from a guilty conscience
> Unto a forest of distrust and fear,
> A darksome place and dangerous to pass:
> There shall you meet with melancholy thoughts,
> Whose baleful humours if you but uphold,
> It will conduct you to despair and death. (III.xi.13–19)

Hieronimo thinks of both revenge and suicide as hellish spiritual journeys; but, as long as his appeals to heaven or his journeys to the court of the King are fruitless, he feels he must choose between evils: "Where shall I run to breathe abroad my woes,/ My woes, whose weight hath wearied the earth?" (III. vii. 1–2). His cries of woe have

> . . . broken through the brazen gates of hell.
> Yet still tormented is my tortur'd soul
> With broken sighs and restless passions,
> That winged mount, and, hovering in the air,
> Beat at the windows of the brightest heavens,
> Soliciting for justice and revenge:
> But they are plac'd in those empyreal heights
> Where, countermur'd with walls of diamond,
> I find the place impregnable, and they
> Resist my woes, and give my words no way. (III.vii.9–18)

If he cannot make his way into heaven, it is clear enough that he has reached hell: "The ugly fiends do sally forth of hell,/And frame my steps to unfrequented paths,/And fear my heart with fierce inflamed thoughts" (III. ii. 16–18).

Hieronimo knows that going to see the King for justice will be a fruitless pilgrimage, and he is tempted to kill himself so he can go a journey to hell for revenge (III. xii. 1–13). Nevertheless he chooses the path that leads to the King; and, when his demand for justice goes unheeded, he gives powerful expression to the force behind all the journeys of the play: "Needs must he go that the devils drive" (III. xii. 82).

In the very next scene the situation is reversed when Hieronimo, who has just decided to seek private revenge, is confronted with other men's appeals for justice, including Bazulto's for his murdered son. Hieronimo is driven temporarily insane, and this loss of control of his spirit sends him on a quest very much like that of the dead spirit of Andrea:

> Though on this earth justice will not be found,
> I'll down to hell, and in this passion
> Knock at the dismal gates of Pluto's court,
> Getting by force, as once Alcides did,
> A troop of Furies and tormenting hags
> To torture Don Lorenzo and the rest.
> .   .   .   .
> Then will I rent and tear them thus and thus,
> Shivering their limbs in pieces with my teeth.
>   *Tear the papers.* (III.xiii.108–13, 122–23.I)

It is most important that Hieronimo denies justice to others as he despairs of justice for himself and turns to revenge: the "limbs" he shivers are actually papers brought to him by men seeking his help in cases at law. All this suggests that a too-obsessive quest for good may be ironically reversed into a journey toward its evil opposite. Just as Balthazar's lust for love leads him to hate and kill, so Hieronimo's love for his son leads to a lust for justice that makes him unjust.

Hieronimo's treatment of Bazulto is even more significant than what he does to the other appellants and their papers. He sees that Bazulto is an image of himself—a "lively portrait"—but this recognition, though it makes him offer pity, does not enable him to help the old man find justice. He regards Bazulto more as a mirror in which he sees his own need than as another man having great importance in his own right. Hieronimo is ashamed to be shown up by a "lesser" man's love for a son (III. xiii. 99). He gives his purse to Bazulto and proposes that they go and sing discordant songs with Isabella, yet for all his pity he cannot respond to the old man's repeated request:

> SENEX. I am a grieved man, and not a ghost,
>   That came for justice for my murder'd son.
> HIER. Ay, now I know thee, now thou nam'st thy son,

> Thou art the lively image of my grief:
> Within thy face, my sorrows I may see. (III.xiii.159–63)

In his madness Hieronimo seems to assume that justice is impossible in Bazulto's case since he feels that it is in his own. Perhaps we are to see that Hieronimo's pity and his grieving for the lost sons is the only response that is truly meaningful under the circumstances, that revenge and justice are equally unsatisfactory. But Hieronimo's pity itself is in part brought on and confused by his mad rage for revenge, and we must therefore also see the way obsessive, self-pitying vengefulness makes him unable to give the help to another man that he asks as an individual in his own right. Hieronimo can see the parallel between his own level and the one "beneath" him, but he cannot consistently see that the levels are really the same. And when he does see a sameness he confuses its real nature.

A man of Hieronimo's high position must see that the "levels" may be a distortion of reality imposed by the ego and by his society's misunderstanding of the traditional idea that a monarchy is a divinely ordained hierarchy in which men are separated in levels according to social class. It must always be remembered that this concept was balanced by the idea that from the *higher perspective* of God in eternity, all men are equal, and particularly so in the face of death.

Hieronimo's conduct is illuminated through the parallel with the Portuguese Viceroy's response to the charge that Alexandro has killed Balthazar. The Viceroy is more self-pitying, perhaps because he is evading his own guilt, and it is clear that his self-concern helps to intensify his vengeful anger to the point where he is unjust to Alexandro. He blames not only this innocent inferior but also Fortune, who he assumes is above him in power. In Act I. iii he attacks Fortune with personal bitterness when he has not yet found any person to blame but himself. Later, when his guilty self-concern is somewhat assuaged by having Alexandro to punish, he speaks in less personal terms, making his complaint against Fortune a universal statement of the tragedy of the man who stands at the highest level of human action:

> Infortunate condition of kings,
> Seated amidst so many helpless doubts!

> First we are plac'd upon extremest height,
> And oft supplanted with exceeding heat,
> But ever subject to the wheel of chance:
> And at our highest never joy we so,
> As we both doubt and dread our overthrow.
> So striveth not the waves with sundry winds
> As fortune toileth in the affairs of kings. (III.i.1–9)

The conception of the tragic as a condition that puts man in the "extremest" depth or height is essential to this play. We are repeatedly called upon to visualize the terrifying extremes of madness and despair, of love and hate, whether on the field of war or in the arbor of peace. Typically, man is brought to the peak of passion and the edge of death, and there we are invited to ponder his fate as he is caught between the extremes of heaven and hell. Andrea is slain in the crisis of the battle. Horatio is brought to a passionate sexual climax and is then killed. The supposed "extreme hate" of Alexandro's heart brings him to the "extremity of death," but, at the latest possible moment, the truth is revealed; and Villuppo is instead made to suffer "the bitterest torments and extremes" (III. i. 16, 31–32, 40, 100). Alexandro is tested and then saved, but Pedringano is deceived to think that he is being tried by extremes and will be saved at the "uttermost" moment:

> Lor. Tell him his pardon is already sign'd,
> And thereon bid him boldly be resolv'd:
> For were he ready to be turned off
> (As 'tis my will the uttermost be tried),
> Thou with his pardon shalt attend him still:
> Show him this box, tell him his pardon's in't. (III.iv.67–72)

The play asks whether man is governed by a benign destiny that lets him suffer only to test and save him if he is patient, or whether destiny is figured forth instead in such men as Lorenzo, such forces as Revenge, who only *seem* to be interested in human welfare. We are asked to ponder this question most deeply in the case of Hieronimo, who is called upon to be just to other men who are in extremes while the failure of justice for his own son's murder drives him to extremes of hatred and of despairing madness:

Thus must we toil in other men's extremes,
That know not how to remedy our own,
And do them justice, when unjustly we,
For all our wrongs, can compass no redress. (III.vi.1–4)

II *Justice and Revenge*

The lines just quoted concisely express Hieronimo's dilemma: as he suffers the extremes of injustice, will he be able to remain just himself; or will the passions that drive a man to seek revenge as a means of obtaining justice inevitably pervert the quest for justice and lead to injustice? [4] We have already studied the psychology of this kind of perversion, and we have seen that Hieronimo is unable to serve justice with Bazulto and the other litigants. But that scene was symbolic action, unrelated to the plot: it may only show the danger that Hieronimo *might* be unjust. Besides, the defeat of justice in that scene is only incidental to the presentation of Hieronimo's madness, and his *pity* for Bazulto may in the last analysis seem more appropriate to the old man's need anyway. For a real understanding of Hieronimo's dilemma, therefore, other questions remain. Is he justified when he finally turns to private revenge, and is he just to his victims? Does he serve justice in the execution of Pedringano? Is he just to the father of Lorenzo and Bel-imperia, the Duke of Castile, whom he murders after the play-within-the-play? Is Revenge an agent of justice, and how is Revenge related to the power of Heaven?

The issue is not really whether Kyd wants us to condemn or to applaud Hieronimo. There is no question that we are made to sympathize with his course of action, and it can be argued that the final chorus of Andrea and Revenge expresses unqualified approval of Hieronimo, since they plan to send him to the eternal pleasures of Elysium. Beyond this, what we are asked to do, I think, is to bring with our sympathies an interest in the working of fate and of the human heart and mind, so that—while we sympathize with Hieronimo as a man suffering the extremest torments and while we can see that he acts naturally according to the pattern of tragic fate and so perhaps "rightly"—at the same time we should see that he acts ironically and becomes the thing he hates. In this respect, as in much else, the play-within-the-play dramatizes in microcosm what the play develops in full: Hieronimo plays the part of the Bashaw who kills Perseda's true love so that

Soliman can try to win her. *Thus he assumes the role of his enemy, Lorenzo,* the friend of Soliman-Balthazar, *and symbolically murders his own son in the very act of revenging his murder.*

We sympathize with Hieronimo for several reasons. We have known him as a sensible man, as a devoted father, and as a loyal agent of his king before he is called upon to become an avenger. Because we know that he loves his son and is very proud of him, we expect him to be shattered when Horatio is killed, and we understand how his grief drives him to talk of both suicide and revenge. We would doubtless have sympathetic understanding if he went directly forth in hot blood and slaughtered the murderers, although we might regard this act as a questionable expression of a man's love for his son. But Hieronimo does not know who the murderers are, and so he must think about what to do.

As he thinks, we are greatly impressed by his concern for justice and other values. He believes that private revenge is an evil sent from hell, and he does not turn to it until all hope is dead that either heaven or the King will give him justice. Then his mind breaks, and when his acceptance of revenge comes, we must pity him. Even then he believes that revenge comes from the underworld, although he wants to associate it with the *judges* Minos, Aeacus, and Rhadamanth when it is really a force that comes into play when they cannot render a fair verdict (cf. I. i and III. xiii. 142–43). How can we not pity Hieronimo even more when his wife is driven to madness and suicide by her grief and when Bel-imperia adds her voice to the chorus of voices urging him on to revenge? We surely sympathize with his wish to feel that heaven approves his revenges, and so we understand when he sees Bel-imperia's joining him as a sign that saints solicit his revenge (IV. i. 30–34). As long as we put ourselves in Hieronimo's place—which is what we must do as fellow humans—we must pity him and give our understanding to the emotions that enable him to tell himself that he is doing heaven's work when he kills. But we must not confine ourselves to looking at the action through Hieronimo's eyes. Our response must in part be to say "There, but for the grace of being in the audience, go I." Our place in the audience puts us on a potentially higher level of awareness than the one Hieronimo occupies. As I have shown earlier, we must not let this greater awareness cut us off from Hieronimo as a form of ourselves: we must know that we would very likely want to act as he does if we were in his place. But we must also know that, just before Hieronimo becomes convinced that heaven's saints "do sit soliciting" for revenge, Revenge has said that *he* is the one who does so:

> Content thyself, Andrea; though I sleep,
> Yet is my mood soliciting their souls:
> Sufficeth thee that poor Hieronimo
> Cannot forget his son Horatio. (III.xv.19–22)

Hieronimo's thinking that he is heaven's agent does not mean that the play is saying that he *is* heaven's agent; it means that a man of Hieronimo's character in his dire circumstances needs desperately to think he is such an agent.

The difference between these two meanings is great: if we equate Hieronimo's ideas with those of the play and of Kyd, we ignore the characterizations and the elaborate structure of levels Kyd has created, and we come away with a statement about revenge that Kyd might better have expressed in two or three concise sentences of an essay. The utterance of a character in a play must ordinarily be assumed to express *his* point of view unless there is real evidence to the contrary. Kyd may not be expressing his personal view of revenge anywhere in the play. A play is a work of dramatic art, and it may well present a multitude of views on the action it contains—a different view for each character. We should not demand that these views be reconciled in a character's statement of "what the author is trying to say." Instead, we should expect that the views of the characters will be expressions of their minds and hearts, and that the views of different characters and the events of the play will interact to illuminate the issues in question.

The greatest value of a tragedy is that it invites us to imagine "What 'tis to be subject to destiny" and provides insights into what makes men think and act as they do (III. xv. 28). In order to direct our attention to this deeper level of insight, it is helpful for the dramatist to leave ironic discrepancies between what the characters think and what the facts are within the story. It need not matter to the writer what the "truth" is at a level beyond human awareness. He can simply use such characters as Revenge to show that the other characters are limited in their awareness, and so to make us think about that awareness and its limitations.

We must therefore not accept Revenge's point of view as final, either, even though his spirit dominates the final speeches of the play and offers judgments of the characters. He, too, is a character in the play, and this implies that his awareness is limited. He thinks he understands and controls the level of action *beneath* him, but we have no reason to believe that he knows his true relation to Proserpina or to the three judges in the underworld or to God in heaven. The play consistently distinguishes the underworld powers from those *above* in heaven: the typical pattern is for Hieronimo to turn away from heaven toward thoughts of the underworld in a hell of torment and despair. Revenge is diabolical in his means, and he kills the guilty and the innocent alike. The only way we can regard Revenge as an agent of God's justice is to contend (with Christian theologians) that even when men and spirits directly oppose themselves to God's "Vindicta Mihi"—vengeance is mine—and seek revenge, they are still somehow compelled to be the instruments of God's will. But such reasoning is not clearly invoked in the play, and insofar as it is implied, it can only assert, as it does in Christian theology, the writer's faith that in the mind of God, *at a level beyond our understanding,* there is no such thing as evil, that all our suffering is somehow part of God's loving plan for us.

What *is* clearly implied in the play is that Revenge may be at a lower level of awareness than we are, since he is a participant in the play as well as an audience. Yet this same line of reasoning must also make us realize that we, like the characters in the play, doubtless err in many of our judgments, since we are to imagine that some of the same minds and forces are above us that are above Hieronimo or Revenge. We must therefore not presume to judge the characters harshly from our superior vantage point in the audience.

Thus Kyd's structure of levels of action and awareness functions in an amazing number of ways which can perhaps be condensed into one essential point in relation to our consideration of Hieronimo: we are to see ourselves in him and yet understand his situation with greater detachment than he can have. That is, we are to know that we might well act as he does, and also know that, in so doing, we would be subject to a destiny that dooms us to a self-deceiving and tragic blindness.

With these matters understood, let us look at Hieronimo's revenge from the higher perspective that enables us to see so much more than he can. For the purposes of this play, at least, Kyd has made Revenge a figure having great power over human destiny, an infernal power that becomes active when men combine the roles of lover and killer. Justice may be impossible when love is replaced by hate, and revenge then may act through a chain of love and hate relationships to destroy both the innocent and the guilty. All this we have discussed earlier, but we have not considered whether there is any *just basis* for revenge in any of the links of the chain. We probably feel that there is little or no justice in the murder of Horatio by Balthazar and Lorenzo, a murder they call "revenge." But is there a just basis for revenging the death of Andrea?—or of Horatio? Now in a sense both of these questions can be answered if we can answer one other question: does Horatio speak the truth when he tells Bel-imperia that Balthazar killed Andrea in a cowardly way? If Horatio lies here, then there is no just need to avenge Andrea, and Horatio is, as Balthazar and Lorenzo say, an ambitious man who is using lies to ingratiate himself with Bel-imperia and to alienate her from Balthazar.

Let us look at the evidence as justly as we can. In Act I.i, Andrea simply says he was killed in battle, and neither he nor the judges in the underworld suggest that he died unjustly. Revenge merely takes over when the judges give Andrea's soul no resting place because he was both a lover and a warrior. In Act I.ii the Spanish General gives a detailed description of the battle, and again there is no indication of foul play in Balthazar's defeat of Andrea. Balthazar is charged with nothing more than vaunting over his fallen foe, a traditional way of simultaneously intimidating and daring surviving enemies.

The first hint that there may have been foul play in the battle comes in Act I. iii, when Villuppo tells the Portuguese Viceroy that Balthazar was shot in the back by Alexandro. We *know* that this story is false and that Villuppo's motive in telling it is to win a reward from the Viceroy at the expense of a rival. Is it only a coincidence that in the very next scene Horatio tells Bel-imperia a parallel story of cowardly murder in battle and wins the reward of her favor at the same time that he sets her in deadly hate against his only rival for her affections?

The Viceroy exits after swearing that he will take revenge on Alexandro, and Villuppo is left alone on stage to explain himself to the audience: "Thus have I with an envious forged tale/Deceiv'd the king, betray'd mine enemy,/And hope for guerdon of my villainy" (I. iii. 93–95). Villuppo then goes off at one door of the stage, and Horatio leads Bel-imperia in at the other. Horatio tells her about the battle, praising Andrea and describing how he, Horatio, defeated Balthazar and rescued Andrea's body to give it loving burial. He produces a scarf Andrea had worn on his arm that he has taken as a token of his friend. He must have known that such scarves were usually worn as tokens of a lady's favor, and we must suspect that he has been playing for Bel-imperia's favor in everything he has said, and especially in the way he has stressed all that he did for Andrea.

The crucial part of Horatio's narrative, however, is the charge that Balthazar took cowardly advantage of Andrea:

> When both our armies were enjoin'd in fight,
> Your worthy chevalier amidst the thick'st,
> For glorious cause still aiming at the fairest,
> Was at the last by young Don Balthazar
> Encounter'd hand to hand: their fight was long,
> Their hearts were great, their clamours menacing,
> Their strength alike, their strokes both dangerous.
> But wrathful Nemesis, that wicked power,
> Envying at Andrea's praise and worth,
> Cut short his life to end his praise and worth.
> She, she herself, disguis'd in armour's mask
> (As Pallas was before proud Pergamus),
> Brought in a fresh supply of halberdiers,
> Which paunch'd his horse and ding'd him to the ground.
> Then young Don Balthazar with ruthless rage,
> Taking advantage of his foe's distress,
> Did finish what his halberdiers begun,
> And left not till Andrea's life was done. (I.iv.9–26)

This description appeals to Bel-imperia in two ways at once by saying that Andrea was overcome because of his great worth and by saying that his worth was so great that he could only be overcome by a cowardly attack (compare the General's "Brave man at arms, but weak to Balthazar" [I. ii. 72]). Andrea is dead, but his image is intact. Horatio's words enable him to usurp that image and the benefits that go with it.

Horatio's narrative is at best a colored one, if not an outright lie. We are not to believe that Horatio literally means that "wrathful Nemesis, that wicked power" enviously intervened *in her own person* to destroy Andrea. Yet, at the same time that this little fiction is the one provably "false" element of Horatio's narrative, it may also be the true key to all the revenges. Balthazar and the Portuguese soldiers were the human agents of Andrea's death, but the real villain at a higher level of action was "Nemesis, that wicked power." And who is Nemesis? Why, the Greek counterpart of Kyd's Revenge. Nemesis punishes those who offend the gods either by committing crimes or by rising to such heights that they earn the envy of the gods. We may thus regard Revenge as the author of *all* the deaths of the play, including the death of Andrea that causes the others. The actor playing Revenge must be sure to smile most of the time.

But who at the human level is envious of those of high worth? There is Villuppo, who has just branded the story he told for reward "envious" [5] as well as "forged." Do not the same terms fit Horatio's story? There is still more evidence indicating that they do. Lorenzo and Balthazar spend a good deal of time trying to figure out why Bel-imperia is so hostile to Balthazar (II. i). When they find that Horatio is her lover, they regard him as an ambitious man who has used deceit to win her heart (II. i. 118–31, II. ii. 41, II. iv. 60). Balthazar and Lorenzo both know that Bel-imperia loved Andrea, yet neither of them ever gives the slightest indication that he thinks Balthazar has given her cause to hate him by killing her love in a cowardly fashion. Balthazar's foolish passions and Lorenzo's cunning both argue against Balthazar's guilt. We might ask why they do not suspect that Bel-imperia hates Balthazar simply for killing Andrea, cowardice or no; but, granted the character of Bel-imperia, she might be expected to love the man who could best Andrea in a fair fight more than she had loved Andrea himself.

And there is yet another bit of evidence: two characters in the play are hanged, Horatio and Pedringano. Are they similar in any other respects? Horatio says he tells Bel-imperia his story about Andrea's death "For love of him and service to yourself" (I. iv. 6). If the story of Villuppo in the preceding scene may have paralleled the falseness and the motive for Horatio's story, what Pedringano says in the following scene may at least parallel its motive; for he speaks of "service" to Lorenzo and hopes to be rewarded for the information he provides (II. i. 42–43, 72, 82, *et passim*). And the parallel between the hanging of Horatio and of Pedringano is more than perfunctory. When Horatio is hanged, Lorenzo says that "Although his life were still ambitious proud,/Yet is he at the highest now he is dead" (II. iv. 60–61). When Lorenzo promises Pedringano advancement for the murder of Serberine, he says: "When things shall alter, as I hope they will,/Then shalt thou mount for this: thou know'st my mind" (III. ii. 92–93). Pedringano does not know Lorenzo's mind, since the "alter" is a play on halter-alter, which can still be homonyms in English; and the "mount" refers to what happens when Pedringano climbs the gallows. Like Horatio, he will be "at the highest" when he dies.

We cannot be sure what to think of Horatio; he may be an ambitious liar, as Lorenzo and Balthazar think, or he may simply be the hero his father and Bel-imperia believe him to be. The important thing is that, while we cannot be sure one way or the other, we have reason to question Hieronimo's adulation of his son—to see the situation not only from Hieronimo's point of view but also from that of his enemies. Nothing can justify to us their murder of Horatio, but our doubt may make us question the justice of seeking revenge for either Andrea or Horatio. When Hieronimo finds Horatio's body hanging in his arbor, he says: "O heavens, why made you night to cover sin?/By day this deed of darkness had not been" (II. v. 24–25). Hieronimo means only to cry out against the murderers, but his words may also apply to Horatio, who was the one, after all, to choose night as the time most appropriate to consummate his love for Bel-imperia, a consummation unblest by the church and therefore a "sin" from the point of view of Heaven (II. iv. 1–5).

If considerations such as these make us wonder whether there is really any just basis for Hieronimo's quest for revenge, they do not make us doubt the sincerity of his belief in his son and in his own cause. And in any case we are likely to accept Hieronimo's killing of Balthazar and Lorenzo because we feel so strongly that they are vicious men. Balthazar may not have taken cowardly advantage of Andrea in the battle, but he and Lorenzo are cowards in their murder of Horatio. We especially hate Lorenzo for his Machiavellian guile; he reaches the depth of evil in his use of the appearance of friendship to conceal murderous intentions. This horror, of which Alexandro is accused by Villuppo, is perhaps the most obviously perverted combination of love and hate that man is capable of. But we have no sooner learned to hate guile of this sort in Lorenzo than Hieronimo takes it up, and this again complicates our judgment of his actions. The long third act is evenly divided between the conclusion of Lorenzo's intrigues and the beginning of those of Hieronimo in reply. The shift of initiative takes place with the hanging of Pedringano, who set Lorenzo in motion by revealing that Horatio was Bel-imperia's lover, and who sets Hieronimo in motion through his letter revealing that Lorenzo and Balthazar murdered Horatio. Then, just as Lorenzo promised to save Pedringano from the gallows, Hieronimo promises to save the hangman from his own noose. Having won the initiative through events that remind us of Lorenzo, Hieronimo convinces himself that he must cloak his hatred of Balthazar and Lorenzo with the appearance of love. In his revenge, he will become a Machiavel like Lorenzo:

> . . . I will revenge his death!
> But how? not as the vulgar wits of men,
> With open, but inevitable ills,
> As by a secret, yet a certain mean,
> Which under kindship will be cloaked best. (III.xiii.20–24)

These lines are part of a very important soliloquy in which Hieronimo works his way to this diabolical policy after starting with the Christian position that God will avenge. The soliloquy marks the crisis of the play, for Hieronimo's abandonment of hope in heavenly or earthly justice turns out to be permanent. During the action that remains, Hieronimo keeps his hatred concealed behind a mask of love until all the masks are ripped off at the end of the play-within-the-play.

In the scene following the crisis, the Duke of Castile takes Lorenzo aside to question him about his treatment of Hieronimo. We come to regard the Duke as a good man when we hear him speak for love and honor in dealings between men. Then Hieronimo enters, and the Duke persuades him to embrace Lorenzo. Although the Duke thinks he has wrought a sincere reconciliation,

Hieronimo and Lorenzo are now both false. Hieronimo wears
his mask so skillfully that he even fools Lorenzo, but at the end
of the scene he makes it plain to the audience that he mistrusts
both Lorenzo and the Duke:

> CAST. Come on, Hieronimo, at my request;
> Let us entreat your company today.
> > *Exeunt [all but* HIERONIMO].
> HIER. Your lordship's to command.—Pha! keep your way.
> *Chi mi fa più carezze che non suole,*
> *Tradito mi ha, o tradir mi vuole.* (III.xiv. 165–69)

Edwards provides the following translation of the Italian: "He
who shows unaccustomed fondness for me has betrayed me or
wants to betray me"—a cynical proverb that describes the way
that Lorenzo and Hieronimo project their own treachery onto
others. When Lorenzo was false to others, he was sure they were
false to him, and so he destroyed Serberine and Pedringano. Now
Hieronimo is false, and he imputes his own falseness to the Duke,
so that the Duke's kindness itself makes him a victim of Hieronimo's mad rage.

We may assent to the deaths of Balthazar and Lorenzo, even
though we see that Hieronimo has to play the part of Lorenzo
to get his revenge, but we cannot feel that the death of the Duke
is a just consequence of the murder of Horatio. The Duke is entirely innocent of that crime, and insofar as he is tainted by having fathered the villainous Lorenzo, we must remember that he is
also the father of Bel-imperia. Yet he is made to suffer the greatest
loss, being compelled to witness the death of both his children
and then to die himself. And the impression that he is an innocent
is maintained to the very end. The King calls for tortures to make
Hieronimo talk, but the Duke neither intends nor expects harm
when he carries a knife to Hieronimo. The Duke thinks Hieronimo wants the knife so he can sharpen his pen, and instead
Hieronimo kills him with it so he can be free to kill himself.

In the course of serving revenge, Hieronimo destroys much that
he has stood for as a father and as an agent of justice. His final act
of suicide is thus implicit in many previous actions, and especially
in his murder of Erastus-Horatio in the play-within-the-play. As
Hieronimo says, his own death is implied by the death of his son:

"They murder'd me that made these fatal marks" (IV.iv. 97). His murder of the Duke, a father like himself, is the last of these symbolic acts of self-murder, and it is followed immediately by his actual suicide.

From our higher perspective, then, we see revenge to be inevitably unjust: self-pity and an obsessive lust for justice tragically blind a man and make him destroy the innocent—even make him think he is doing what heaven wants when we can see that he is the agent of a figure sent from the underworld. Hieronimo's murder of the innocent Duke is a natural part of the working of Revenge or Nemesis, who draws everyone within reach into a maelstrom of terror and bloodshed. The conflict begins in the battle between Spain and Portugal, then narrows to a combat between Andrea and Balthazar, and finally widens again until it involves men only remotely connected with those two.

III *Tragic Nemesis*

For the broader purposes of Revenge or Nemesis, which transcend the question of Hieronimo's justice, the battle of Andrea and Balthazar is only a part of a larger battle that includes all the people of Spain and Portugal: Revenge is an extension of the war, bringing both countries to ruin (IV. iv. 202–17). When Hieronimo is convinced at last that revenge is what heaven wants, he seems also to adopt a wider goal of destroying nations: "Now shall I see the fall of Babylon,/Wrought by the heavens in this confusion" (IV. i. 195–98). During the Reformation, Protestants compared Roman Catholic countries with the Babylonian Empire of the Old Testament. To an Elizabethan audience in the decade of the Spanish Armada, Hieronimo's reference to the fall of Babylon would probably have seemed an appropriate interpretation of the action of the play as showing Spain suffering for having become "no world; but mass of public wrongs,/Confus'd and fill'd with murder and misdeeds," a world cut off from communion with the "sacred heavens" (III. ii. 3–5).

The enactment of the fall of Babylon in a playlet having a "confusion" of foreign languages must also remind us of the failure of the tower of Babel (Gen. 11). In the Old Testament of the Geneva Bible, the name of the city of Babylon is always Babel.[6] The association of the two sounds is natural in any case, and Kyd could expect his audience to make the connection in

this context. The confusion of tongues at Babel was God's punishment for the pride that makes men seek to be like gods, as in *The
Spanish Tragedy* men usurp God's justice or seek to make puppets
of their fellow men. The confusion of tongues at Babel is also a
powerful symbol of the futility of trying to use language to reach
out to each other from our isolation as individuals. In the playlet
each actor is confined within the foreign language assigned him
by Hieronimo. This epitomizes the failure of words elsewhere in
the play that finally leads Hieronimo to bite his tongue out after
he has tried to explain his revenge to the King and his court and
they will not or cannot understand him.

The tragically isolated individuals who inhabit the world of
The Spanish Tragedy are so busy using words as tools to deceive
each other that they do not so much talk *to* each other as *at* each
other.[7] Often they speak aside or deliver monologues that ignore
their interlocutor. They do not really open up until they are alone,
and then their words often deceive themselves. "Words have several works" (III. i. 17). Words cleverly used as tools can help to
win services and rewards in affairs of love and hatred alike. The
artificial and indirect verbal "ambages" of Balthazar are poor
wooers (I. iv. 90–91, II. i. 14), but Horatio's words of courtship
conquer Balthazar in love, just as his sword did in war:

> . . . in that war he gave me dangerous wounds,
> And by those wounds he forced me to yield,
> And by my yielding I became his slave.
> Now in his mouth he carries pleasing words,
> Which pleasing words do harbour sweet conceits,
> Which sweet conceits are lim'd with sly deceits,
> Which sly deceits smooth Bel-imperia's ears,
> And through her ears dive down into her heart,
> And in her heart set him where I should stand. (II.i.121–29)

Villuppo's false story, Lorenzo's cleverness with Pedringano, and
Horatio's courtship of Bel-imperia lead ironically to their un-
doing: because of the perversity of the human will, the use of
words as tools to manipulate people brings the opposite of the
desired result. Hieronimo does not bite his tongue out until the
end, but he sometimes doubts the ability of words to express
the heart's grief or to obtain justice (III. ii. 67, III. vii. 67–73). His
complaints and appeals for justice affect nature and are heard by

Revenge sent from hell, but the heavens seem as deaf to his words
as the King is:

> Where shall I run to breathe abroad my woes,
> My woes, whose weight hath wearied the earth?
> Or mine exclaims, that have surcharg'd the air
> With ceaseless plaints for my deceased son?
> The blust'ring winds, conspiring with my words,
> At my lament have mov'd the leaveless trees,
> Disrob'd the meadows of their flower'd green,
> Made mountains marsh with spring-tides of my tears,
> And broken through the brazen gates of hell.
> Yet still tormented is my tortur'd soul
> With broken sighs and restless passions,
> That winged mount, and, hovering in the air,
> Beat at the windows of the brightest heavens,
> Soliciting for justice and revenge:
> But they are plac'd in those empyreal heights
> Where, countermur'd with walls of diamond,
> I find the place impregnable, and they
> Resist my woes, and give my words no way. (III.vii.1–18)

This passage demonstrates, as it also defines, both the power of
words and their futility. Hieronimo's passionate eloquence should
be able to move all but the heartless or the dead, and yet his only
audience within the play consists of heartless Revenge and the
ghost of Andrea.

The confusion of words is epitomized not only in the play-
within-the-play at the end, but also in the conflicting accounts of
the battle from which the whole action springs. The image of man
in battle expresses Kyd's vision of the tragic nearly as well·as the
playlet does. Andrea's love for Bel-imperia has carried him onto
the field of hate, where he and Balthazar are caught with other
men in a great welter of violence and yet are isolated from all
others in the deadly rivalry of single combat.

Or so we suppose at first, only to have the picture darkened for
us by the dubious words of Villuppo and Horatio, until finally
all is enveloped in the smoke of "mystery." Andrea died and Balthazar lived; Spain won and Portugal lost. Why? What forces determine the fate of individuals and of nations? We can never be
sure whether it was the strength and valor of the soldiers or their

guile and cowardice. Or were there forces at work that could not
be recognized in the passionate darkness of battle? The victorious
Spaniards naturally and gratefully attribute their victory to the
justice of heaven; the defeated Portuguese as naturally try to
blame fickle Fortune (cf. I. ii. 6–14, 138–40; I. iii. 10–26). The
force that appeals most strongly to our imaginations is personified
in the mysterious figure of Revenge who presides over the entire
play in much the same way as the shadowy Nemesis may determine the outcome of battle. Nemesis or Revenge manipulates
humans who become like the power above them in becoming its
agents, using deceit and violence to satisfy a deadly malice.

In *The Spanish Tragedy* equitable justice fails, but there is a
predictable retributive element within the tragic mystery of the
human condition. This element may be seen as the irony of fate:
Horatio's expectation of the "death" of love is fulfilled only in a
literal death, Balthazar's murderous attempt to win Bel-imperia's
love increases her hate, Lorenzo's efforts to make himself safe
lead to his doom, and Hieronimo's desire to destroy Lorenzo for
love of his son drives him to make a new Lorenzo of himself and
to re-enact the murder of his son. Many critics have proposed
that ironic inevitability is an essential aspect of destiny in all
tragedies, and they are probably right. But then we want to know
why tragic destiny is ironic.

For Kyd, although not necessarily for all writers, tragic destiny
is ironic because an individual's very effort to impose his will on
destiny is self-defeating. When men or nations act as isolated individuals in neglect of the wills of the gods and other men, they
lose the capacity to act successfully even as individuals.[8] The
passions that drive a man to willful individualism also blind him,
and the egotism of tragic individualism is in itself a passion that
blocks a person's understanding of himself as it also turns others
against his will. In failing to see others as forms of himself, the
tragic individual again loses the ability to know his own heart because he rejects the chance to learn from the experience of others.
A man deifies his own will when he regards himself as cause, all
others as effects or mere puppets, and in his hubris forgets "what
'tis to be subject to destiny" as he loses sight of the complex way
the passions and motives of many men interact to produce the
mysterious patterns of life that are willed by the gods.

CHAPTER 3

The Smoke of Battle

ACT I of *The Spanish Tragedy* serves as exposition in a deeper sense than is usual, for it is not only an introduction to the play as a whole but a microcosm of it. It is necessary to make only a few distortions and omissions to show a striking parallel between the whole play and the first act:

1) *The Play:* The central action of the play begins with the murder of Horatio, the lover of Bel-imperia, by Balthazar and his friends. This murder is followed by a conflict between Lorenzo and Hieronimo in which Hieronimo appeals to the King for justice. Justice fails, and the wrathful father seeks blood revenge. The play ends with the consummation of this revenge in Hieronimo's play-within-the-play which includes wooing and is itself a microcosm of the whole.

2) *Act I:* The "action" of the exposition begins before the start of the play with the slaying of Andrea, the lover of Bel-imperia, by Balthazar and his friends. This slaying is followed by a conflict between Lorenzo and the combination of Horatio and Hieronimo in which Hieronimo appeals to the King for justice (I. ii). In the next scene justice fails and a wrathful father, the Portuguese Viceroy, seeks blood revenge. The act ends with wooing and with Hieronimo's playlet about English conquests of Spain and Portugal. This playlet is a microcosm of the whole in using images of hate and conquest to promote amity.

These parallels are important in several ways. As I have argued in Chapter II, parallelism itself is central to both the structure and the theme of *The Spanish Tragedy*. The play implies that men must perceive parallel relationships as well as those of cause and effect if they would understand reality and their place in it. Although I may have had to strain to show an overall parallel of Act I with the play as a whole, there can be no doubt of several of the similarities I have suggested. We must observe the parallel between Andrea and Horatio if we are to understand the play at all. The action is to avenge Andrea, but it does so only through Hieronimo's revenge for his son, Horatio, who re-creates in the action of the play the prior roles of Andrea as lover of Bel-imperia and as victim of Balthazar. This parallel suggests that the power of Revenge works to make the present a repetition of the past. We seem to live in a multi-dimensional house of mirrors in which every mirror is a doorway to an understanding of destiny and of ourselves.

A second inescapable parallel between Act I and the play as a whole is that between Hieronimo's appeals for justice in behalf of Horatio in Act I. ii and in Act III. xii. In the first case, both Lorenzo and Horatio claim Balthazar as a prisoner, and the King is called upon to settle the dispute. Hieronimo intervenes in behalf of Horatio, introducing the question whether personal involvement may interfere with fair judgment. The King assures Hieronimo that Horatio will not be wronged and proposes a compromise that is acceptable to all, although it actually favors Lorenzo's claim more than his contribution to the capture of Balthazar warrants. This decision of the King may be viewed as an exposition or foreshadowing of what is to follow. Indeed, every scene of Act I presents a problem of justice in order to introduce this as a major theme of the play. At the same time, the repetition is another suggestion that the links in the chain of an avenging fate are all alike, that the temporal pattern of revenge may be one of recurrence.

If the first two parallels suggest the identity of different times of existence, the third, between the Viceroy's cry for revenge in Act I. iii and Hieronimo's in Acts II–IV, implies that tragic fate is the same in different places. Again we may say that the Viceroy's vengeful fury against Alexandro for the supposed murder of Balthazar foreshadows what is to follow for Hieronimo, but we must also note that it helps us to *interpret* the action to follow: Kyd's point may be that the Viceroy is a form of Hieronimo, as Horatio is of Andrea. The Portuguese scene follows the preceding one not only in the logic of alternating the locale between the two courts, but also in the thematic logic that says the Spanish King's mild partiality should lead to the Viceroy's extreme injustice, which in turn should lead to Bel-imperia's talk of revenge in scene iv. The scenes seem to involve different people, but the

Viceroy's passions and actions fit into the passions and actions of the others to create one continuous line of thematic development showing how personal involvement may lead to a lust for justice that demands revenge.

The last of the parallels between Act I and the rest of the play is the one between Hieronimo's dumbshow in the last scene of Act I and his play-within-the-play in the last act. Act I and the play-within-the-play stand at opposed extremes of the play, but each is a microcosm that works like a mirror to reflect the other and the play as a whole. When a person stands between two mirrors that face each other, each mirror reflects not only his image but also an infinite receding and diminishing series of reflected images of that primary image. This complicated pattern may imply that, beyond the parallels we have seen, lie many others that we will come to as we study the play more closely.

The dumbshow of Spanish and Portuguese defeats in Act I. iv is a "mystery" the Spanish King cannot understand. In this it marks Act I as a unit returning full circle to Revenge's promise at the outset that he would unfold his mystery for Andrea. When we have reached Hieronimo's dumbshow, the first unit of exposition is completed. The mystery has begun to unfold, but only to reveal still more mysteries.

Act I is also marked as a dramatic unit by the strong parallels between its scenes. Each of the four scenes contains some mention of the battle between the Spanish and the Portuguese in which Balthazar killed Andrea and was then captured by Horatio. In every scene someone makes a judgment between two rival claims of what is supposed to have happened in the battle. As we progress through the act, the scenes become increasingly specific in exposition and dramatic in structure and action. All but the last few lines of the first scene are taken up by Andrea's narrative. Although the entire play is implicit in Revenge's promise that Andrea will see Bel-imperia kill Balthazar, no dramatic action occurs on the stage at all, and no specific sequence of action is introduced. In the second scene the account of the battle by the Spanish General is detailed and specific, in contrast to Andrea's mere mention of it in scene i. The exposition gradually focuses on a central issue of these four scenes: what really happened in the battle? The General's account is detailed, but it is impersonal in comparison with the accounts of Villuppo and Horatio in the next two scenes. This movement from vagueness to detailed objectivity to emotional involvement of the narrator is one pattern that defines the increasingly dramatic quality of the successive scenes of Act I.

After the Spanish General completes his narrative of the battle, we are introduced to the King and to Hieronimo, and then the first *dramatized* conflict of the play occurs in the rivalry of Horatio and Lorenzo over the capture of Balthazar (we must not forget that the narratives have *described* a great and bloody conflict between whole armies). But, although this dramatic conflict gives us some idea of the characters of Horatio, Lorenzo, Balthazar, Hieronimo, and the King and although it introduces us to the problem of justice, it does no more than hint of the possibility of later conflict. The scene does not call for any specific further action since the conflict is ended to everyone's apparent satisfaction. Only in scene iv might we suspect that Horatio is not happy.

Scene iii takes us to Portugal for the Viceroy's sorrows, Villuppo's viciously false account of the battle, and the Viceroy's condemnation of Alexandro based on that account. Again the scene itself is a virtually completed conflict that seems to call for no further action beyond the mere fact of Alexandro's execution. A later reversal is implied only if we remember that Villuppo is not only accusing Alexandro falsely but that Balthazar is in fact living, and it is not clear that Kyd expects us to have this in mind, since even to think of it is to see Villuppo's whole scheme as the merest foolishness and to be at least a little annoyed with Kyd for making a guileful villain such an idiot as to risk his life on the chance that Balthazar was killed.

Nevertheless, the scene is truly dramatic, as I have shown in Chapter I. Like the earlier scenes, it focuses on an act of judgment; but the characters and issues are more sharply defined and fully developed. In Act I. ii, the characters of the King and Hieronimo are only roughed in; the Portuguese Viceroy is more fully alive. The issue at stake and the emotions aroused in the Spanish scene seem equally slight when they are compared with those of the Portuguese scene, where passions are violent and the issue is one of life and death.

Despite its raw conflict, scene iii seems more expository than scene iv, however. The Viceroy's lamentations and the stiff, balanced structure of the conflict have a formality about them which, joined with the scene's status as a subplot and with our slight knowledge of Alexandro and Villuppo as people, deprives the action of our full involvement and interest. When we come to scene iv, we have already met all the principal characters save Belimperia, and we have heard something about her. The scene has a complex structure that is an organic outgrowth of its inner action of rivalry. Most important of all, it is the first scene to demand potentially complex action to follow. Bel-imperia listens to Horatio's account of the battle and chooses him over Balthazar as a lover. Through her love for Horatio, Bel-imperia will seek revenge against Balthazar. Countering this, Lorenzo will devise a way to dispel the moods he supposes have led Bel-imperia to reject Balthazar.

The act ends with the Spanish and Portuguese banqueting in celebration of peace. A war between nations is ending while a war between individuals is just starting.[1] The dumbshow that Hieronimo stages for the banquet reflects the function and form of Act I in its exposition of mysteries and in its lack of dramatic development. Act I has introduced mysteries of plot, of character, and of theme. The mystery that plagues Lorenzo and Balthazar even more in Act II. i. is: who or what is making Bel-imperia reject Balthazar? (When they find out, the mystery confronts Hieronimo: who killed Horatio?) More a matter of theme is the mystery of the battle: What really happened, and what forces determined the outcome? And what is justice? Is it possible? What is its relation to revenge? How does revenge work? Is justice possible for a person who goes to war for his love, or for one who takes personal hatreds home from the field of battle? What is the soul of man, and what is its place in reality that he should act as he does?

Act I, Scene i

The last of these mysteries is the root question of all tragedy, and one answer to it is implicit in the opening lines of the play:

> ANDREA. When this eternal substance of my soul
> Did live imprison'd in my wanton flesh,
> Each in their function serving other's need,
> I was a courtier in the Spanish court. (I.i.1–4)

The soul of man is an eternal substance, but it cannot live in the flesh without being in a relation to the flesh in which each helps

the other. Entirely isolated, *independent* existence implies death.
The human tragedy of passion arises from the paradox that the
soul lives imprisoned in wanton or uncontrolled flesh. The paradox is the traditional idea that the substance of the soul is by nature akin to things pure and orderly, so that the flesh, by its very
nature of being wanton, becomes a prison for a substance that is
free only within orderly discipline. When a man is alive, the condition of his soul is in part determined by functions of the "wanton flesh," such as the passions of love and hate. A man must see
relationships not only between himself and other men and the
powers above men but also between the elements that make up
his nature. As usual, Pedringano illustrates the extreme case of a
man so blinded by a bodily want that he is completely oblivious
to the relation of body to soul:

HANGM[AN] . . . Methinks
                 you should rather hearken to your soul's health.
PED.   Why, sirrah hangman? I take it, that that is good
                 for the body is likewise good for the soul: and it
                 may be, in that box is balm for both.
HANGM.   Well, thou art even the merriest piece of man's
                 flesh that e'er groaned at my office door.
                 . . . .
HIER.   I have not seen a wretch so impudent!
                 O monstrous times, where murder's set so light,
                 And where the soul, that should be shrin'd in heaven,
                 Solely delights in interdicted things,
                 Still wand'ring in the thorny passages
                 That intercepts itself of happiness.
                 . . . .
DEP.   So, executioner; convey him hence,
                 But let his body be unburied.
                 Let not the earth be choked or infect
                 With that which heaven contemns and men neglect.
                              (III.vi.74–80, 89–94, 105–8)

Hieronimo sees that heaven is the proper home of the soul, but
that souls nonetheless wander in interdicted passages. His words
apply to Lorenzo, Balthazar, and himself as well as to Pedringano. Perhaps they apply most directly of all to Andrea, the
soul without a home even in the underworld, who is forced to re-

turn to earth with Revenge for a companion. The experience of
Andrea parallels the action of the other characters and especially
of Horatio and Hieronimo.

Andrea, who has gone to war for his love, is the first instance of
a person attempting to combine the roles of lover and killer. If we
understand the true relations of body to soul and of passion to
passion, what judgment will we make of such a person's soul? Is
he so much at variance with nature that he must convulse an entire human society? Evidently so, for such a convulsion is the consequence of the failure of justice in the underworld, as I have
shown in Chapter II. As Hieronimo's soul mingles love and hate
and as it passes beyond justice to revenge in the play-within-the-
play, so Andrea's soul must pass beyond the judges of the underworld, following paths that lead him finally to Revenge in a play.

The trip to the land of the dead is the last of life's journeys, the
one that defines life as a journey or passage from a here to a there
that are separate conditions (I. i. 17). But the idea of a journey
may imply that death is not an *end* of existence. Once the journey
of life is over, there is the journey into the underworld for reward
or punishment. Or a person's spirit may return to earth and take
some indirect part in the life continuing there. But he can no
longer return to the relation of things that he knew when he was
alive: "Death's winter nipp'd the blossoms of my bliss,/Forcing
divorce betwixt my love and me" (I. i. 13–14).

The idea that the dead are divorced from their love includes
being cut off from the old emotions as well as from people. In the
play, Andrea's love for Bel-imperia is never expressed as much
more than friendship; and at the end, exulting in her death with
the others, he cares only that her ghost should be happy in the
afterlife. If the emotions of the dead are changed, so even more
are those of the living with regard to them. One of the main dis-
ruptions of relationship is death's divorce of love from its object
and the transformation of its passion into hatred of those who
killed the loved one, a pattern studied in different forms in Hieronimo and in Bel-imperia.

Andrea's formal and impersonal narrative of the journey to the
underworld is adapted from Book VI of Virgil's *Aeneid*. The style
is derived from that of earlier English adaptations of Virgil, such
as Sackville's Induction to the metrical tragedy of the Duke of
Buckingham in the *Mirror for Magistrates*.[2] The power and the

limitations of Kyd's more usual style can be felt at once, however, in Andrea's first lines, before he turns to Virgil:

> When this eternal substance of my soul
> Did live imprison'd in my wanton flesh,
> Each in their function serving other's need,
> I was a courtier in the Spanish court.
> My name was Don Andrea, my descent,
> Though not ignoble, yet inferior far
> To gracious fortunes of my tender youth:
> For there in prime and pride of all my years,
> By duteous service and deserving love,
> In secret I possess'd a worthy dame,
> Which hight sweet Bel-imperia by name.
> But in the harvest of my summer joys
> Death's winter nipp'd the blossoms of my bliss,
> Forcing divorce betwixt my love and me. (I.i.1–14)

The passage consists of four groups of lines, having four lines, three lines, four lines, and three lines, respectively. Although each of the four groups of lines is unified by ornamental devices of rhetoric, such as alliteration, the passage is not so formal in its rhetoric as many others because it tells a story rather than developing a logical sequence or an argument. In imagery, flow of language, and syntactic devices, the passage stresses that a past life is described and that its *time* was unnaturally interrupted. The structure of the first four-line unit insists on the distinction between past and present: "When this . . ./Did live . . ./. . ./I was . . ." The succeeding three-line unit stresses the fact that Andrea's "descent" or ancestry, his inheritance from the *past*, was lower than the height to which he *grew* in "tender youth" as Bel-imperia's lover. At the middle of this capsule version of his career Andrea has reached an apex which links the first seven lines and the next seven: "To gracious fortunes of my tender youth:/For there in prime and pride of all my years." The imagery of the second unit of seven lines suggests the unnatural quality of death in youth by making winter come out of season to nip the blossoms of bliss. The horror of death in youth is later an important element in the lamentation of parents over their dead children, from whom they have perhaps always been cut off by the lack of understanding created by the separation of the generations in time. Time is one of the dimensions that in many ways isolates individuals from each other, although plot parallels between different times and ages imply the ultimate unity of all human experience, as for example when old Hieronimo re-enacts young Lorenzo's crime in the play-within-the-play.

The movement and sense of the passage as a whole is reflected in the sequence of the first lines of each of the four units:

> When this . . . my soul/ Did live . . . .
> My name was Don Andrea . . .
> For there in prime and pride of all my years . . . .
> But in the harvest of my summer joys . . .

The large logical signposts of the passage are obviously "When," "For," and "But." The internal structure of the lines is equally obvious. Alliteration and other echo devices are consistently used to link related elements, usually two to a line: the "*soul*" and its "*substance*," perhaps "*imprison'd*" and "*wanton*," "*their*" and "*other*," too obviously "*court*ier" and "*court*." The chief effect of these first four lines, however, is in the power of the first two lines, the resounding run-on pair that touch off the excitement to follow.

In the second unit, one of three lines, the alliteration has greater complexity: "*Don Andrea*" is linked with "*descent*," "*ignoble*" with "*inferior*," but also "*ignoble*, . . . inferior *far*" is linked with the contrasting "*gracious fortunes*" of the next line. In the third unit, one of four lines, the passage rises to its moment of fulfillment at "In secret I possess'd." Kyd builds up to this climax by joining the use of expansive parallels with alliteration in "*prime* and *pride*" and "*duteous service* and *deserving* love," then dwells upon the climax in the rhyme of "dame" and "name." Other possible implications of the lines are hinted at through the alliteration. How closely related are the "service," the "secret," the "sweet," and the "summer"? But we are not allowed to dwell on such questions, for the last unit, like the first, begins with a pair of resounding run-on lines to mark the sudden swiftness and the terrible reversal of death. These lines reach an alliterative climax in "*blossoms* of my *bliss*," and their power is resolved in the more deliberate rhythm of the final line, where the alliteration on *bl* is split into "*betwixt*" and "*love*" to celebrate the "*divorce*" that "*force*" has wrought between "*my* love" and "*me*."

Act I, Scene ii

At the end of scene i we and Andrea sit down to watch the "mystery" of the tragedy, to "imagine what 'tis to be subject to destiny." But what is destiny? Is it all summed up in Revenge or retribution? The dramatist gives an imaginative vision of the complexity of the human condition, providing insights into a variety of human responses to the workings of destiny. Scene ii begins with the question whether Fortune or the just God of heaven caused the Spanish victory in the war with Portugal. When the outcome is still in doubt, the King asks whether Fortune gave his side victory (I. ii. 6). Once he is told that he is the victor, it is easy for him to see the triumph as an act of a just God (10–11).

The King offers a reward to the Spanish General to tell the story of the battle, introducing a motif of payment for words that please which is to continue through Act II. i, when Pedringano reveals the love of Bel-imperia and Horatio to Lorenzo. The key words in the first ten lines or so of the General's account are "jointly knit/Their frontiers, leaning on each other's bound" and the many repetitions of "both" (22–29, cf. III. xiii. 171). These words imply that Spain and Portugal are interdependent and nearly interchangeable. Yet each thinks itself an independent power. The countries are like the people of the play who think themselves to be the masters of their fates and fail to see others as forms of themselves. Because Portugal has been the vassal state, its destiny appears at first to be a smaller parallel, a subordinate form of the action taking place in the Spanish court. Then, when the Portuguese prince can hope his son will be king of Spain, the two countries are joined in the action as equals.

According to the General's story, the fortunes of war favored neither side until Balthazar conquered Andrea. Andrea had simply spoken of how "life to death made passage through my wounds." The General gives more detail, but he does not allow his narrative to become very emotional; he merely recounts the way Balthazar first defeated Andrea, then was defeated in turn by Horatio. His story clarifies the relation of the national conflict between Spain and Portugal to the personal conflict between Horatio and Balthazar: the defeat of Balthazar meant the defeat of Portugal. In this we may see that the nations are conceived as tragic individuals; it is *The Spanish Tragedy*, not *The Tragedy of Hieronimo, Marshal of Spain*. Yet Spain falls more through inter-

nal conflict than external conflict; for Balthazar soon becomes a
vassal to Lorenzo, and brother wages war against sister, Marshal
against King, until the royal courts have committed suicide as
surely as Hieronimo has. The battlefield is thus an image of man's
tragic condition, and the great warrior and his nation are symbolically interchangeable. It is no wonder that, with the defeat of
his country, the Portuguese Viceroy dreams that his son has been
killed.

When the General concludes his story of the battle, the King
ostentatiously rewards him by giving him a chain from his own
neck, then turns to Hieronimo, promising him that neither he nor
Horatio "shall die without reward:/What means the warning of
this trumpet's sound?" (100–1). The warning is prophetic since it
announces Balthazar's entrance with Horatio and Lorenzo: Horatio will die without reward because of the ascendancy of Lorenzo and Balthazar over him.

There is a significant parallel-in-contrast between this scene
and the one that follows in which the Viceroy blames Fortune for
his defeat and then Villuppo claims a reward for his account of
the battle. It is quite understandable that the losers should squabble among themselves in order to evade individual responsibility
for loss. In the Spanish court we see how men can just as easily, if
more politely, squabble over the spoils of victory. The movement
of the scene shows Kyd's insight into human behavior. Once they
have thanked God for victory, the Spanish begin to congratulate
themselves. The General is rewarded, and the victory belongs to
Horatio. At this happy moment the King reaches out to Hieronimo as very nearly an equal (96–97). The cause of division between the King and Hieronimo is subtly suggested in the King's
inability to recognize Horatio when he sees him, perhaps an instance of the play's pattern showing that the man who thinks he
is master of those beneath him is blind to their identity (110–19).
Blissfully imperceptient to the dangers latent in the situation, the
King rewards each soldier and extends a most gracious welcome
to victors and vanquished alike. Balthazar's reply introduces the
first sour note of the scene as it begins the first dialogue of truly
dramatic conflict in the play:

> The trespass that my father made in peace
> Is now controll'd by fortune of the wars:
> And cards once dealt, it boots not ask why so:

His men are slain, a weakening to his realm,
His colours seiz'd, a blot unto his name,
His son distress'd, a corsive to his heart:
These punishments may clear his late offense. (138–44)

The victor has praised the just God and his own skill; now the loser blames his defeat on bad luck. The other characters speak naturally, but Balthazar is marked from the beginning as a person whose extreme artificiality of speech expresses his superficial character. His only other speech of any length in this scene has the same structure of parallel lines that balance in the middle:

[KING.] Say worthy prince, to whether didst thou yield?
BAL.   To him in courtesy, to this perforce:
         He spake me fair, this other gave me strokes:
         He promis'd life, this other threaten'd death:
         He wan my love, this other conquer'd me:
         And truth to say I yield myself to both.   (160–65)

Horatio and Lorenzo have both claimed Balthazar as a prisoner. His reply suggests the ambivalence of his position in Spain as a prisoner who is also a guest, "gracious" in the "sight" of the King (150). The King hopes that "peace will grow the stronger for these wars"—that love can be advanced by means of, or at least in spite of, hate (146). But, like the chivalric knight who goes to war for his love, or the revenger who kills for love of the dead, the nation that thinks war can advance peace is caught in a tragic transformation of values. Balthazar's speech depicts the past defeat of Balthazar between Lorenzo and Horatio and also looks forward to the future conflict of the three young men. Balthazar will again be defeated by Horatio and by Lorenzo's perverse friendship, which masters his spirit and makes him murder for his love.

The balanced lines of Balthazar's speech leave the scales of justice poised between Horatio and Lorenzo. Hieronimo intervenes to acknowledge that he, as father of Horatio, might be partial; but by the ambiguity of the syntax he also discreetly hints that the King should take care not to be partial (166–69). His appeal urges the King to probe beneath what his high position and his relation to Lorenzo allow him to see, for he must come to the true identity of people in their deeds (170–72). Earlier in the scene the King invited Hieronimo to "frolic" with him because of Horatio's merit in battle (96–97, 126–27). Now he reverses himself and implicitly denies absolute belief in Horatio's rights when he promises justice to him because of *Hieronimo's* merit (173–74).

The issue the King has been called upon to judge is not at all insignificant, for these are not merely two soldiers quarreling over booty. The moral and political bases for the society are in question, since the hierarchy of King and nobles depends on reciprocal rights and duties: each man in the hierarchy owes loyal services to those above him and just rewards to those below. If the King is unjust to Horatio, he threatens the whole structure of society. But there is also a second issue: does the state owe its greatest debt to the strong man with the sword or to the man who steps in after the battle and smiles in order to palliate the use of force and seal the conquest with seeming amity? And, regardless of who deserves the most, there is the interest of the state itself in the matter: the King is an interested party as well as a judge in the dispute. Neither Horatio nor Hieronimo nor the King regards Balthazar fully as a person, or as a form of himself. To Horatio and his father, Balthazar is an object that should bring honor and reward for its heroic captor. Their vision is also limited by their inability to see how things look to those above them in the political hierarchy. The King is able to take their view of Balthazar into account and also to see that Balthazar has great political value. Or we might say that the King's personal vision includes the political interests of the state with which he is identified in a special way.

The King gives Horatio Balthazar's armor and ransom, but Lorenzo is to have his weapons and horse, and he is to have custody of the prince, for Balthazar is to be a guest, and must be entertained by a person of high rank. The King's judgment is not entirely fair to the deserts of Horatio, and this fact illustrates the virtual impossibility of complete justice to the individual. But, as I have just argued, the King is not necessarily being partial to Lorenzo as an individual; he may simply be doing the most judicious thing he can to achieve two political goals at once: 1) to reward Horatio and Lorenzo according to their rank as well as their merit and so keep the hierarchy intact, and 2) to improve relations with Portugal, a goal which will soon lead to the proposal that Balthazar and Bel-imperia marry.

The paradox of the prisoner-guest is one of the play's images that defines the mingling and confusion of love and hate. The use of the image for Balthazar's situation in Spain may remind us vaguely of the predicament of the soul, imprisoned in the wanton flesh of the body and almost inevitably corrupted (I. i. 1–2). The soul of Balthazar could then be imagined to undergo something like a morality-play experience: first, he is tempted by the Flesh in Bel-imperia ("the power of beauty"?); then Lorenzo, who lends himself to comparison with the Vice of the morality play, offers devilishly "wise" counsel in which he tempts his victim to murder.

The scene ends on a note of apparent amity as Balthazar asks Horatio's company, "Whom I admire and love for chivalry" (194). Balthazar lacks either a political or a truly personal perception of life. He approaches life at the level of conventional codes. For him, warfare is governed by chivalry; and he sees no reason why he and Horatio should not be friends. He approaches love by way of the codes of the Petrarchan cult, and he can never speak from the heart—only from the conventions of rhetoric. Having 'no real heart of personality and character himself, he is unable to sense the heart and its motives in others; and he therefore becomes their victim and puppet.

Act I, Scene iii

Scene iii, already discussed in detail in Chapters I and II, functions as a parallel and a bridge between scenes ii and iv. The Portuguese Viceroy must make a judgment about Villuppo's accusation that Alexandro murdered Balthazar, a case in which he is much more personally than politically concerned, and his emotional state completely blocks justice. Thus this scene carries forward the pattern through which personal, political, and conventional modes of behavior are being defined and illustrated in relation to one another. In the next scenes we will see that the enmity of Bel-imperia and Horatio against Balthazar, a personal hatred for the two of them, is in conflict with the King's political desire to marry Bel-imperia and Balthazar. The efforts of Bel-imperia and Hieronimo to obtain justice are consistently opposed, therefore, to efforts to obtain a lasting peace among the people of two countries. It is no simple matter to judge what should be done when justice to individuals cannot be reconciled with the peace of nations.

Through these scenes there is a narrowing of focus from macrocosm to microcosm: scene i made us feel the claims of supernatural powers as well as of humans, and scene ii made us feel the claims of nations as well as individuals; but the later scenes of Act I mostly show us how personal motives sweep all else before them. The Viceroy thinks of his position in personal terms:

> But wherefore sit I in a regal throne?
> This better fits a wretch's endless moan. *Falls to the ground.*
> Yet this is higher than my fortunes reach,
> And therefore better than my state deserves. (I.iii.8–11)

He is concerned for himself and *his position,* not for the throne he leaves without a responsible ruler: as an individual he may be deprived of his crown: "Yes, Fortune may bereave me of my crown" (18). The governing words here are "me" and "my" (cf. 23–27); and, when he does recognize his responsibility for what has happened to his country, it is only to pass beyond that concern to a concern for his son and so, again, for himself (33–42).

Act I, Scene iv

It is no criticism of the play to say that the character of Horatio is ambiguous. He can be considered as an aggressive but honest man or as one who seeks to win Bel-imperia's affections by false means. Or, best of all, he can be viewed in a way that preserves his ambiguity. I have argued in Chapter II that there are reasons to suspect that his account of the battle is little more accurate than Villuppo's. He certainly tells his story in a way that is calculated to please Bel-imperia, glorifying Andrea's role in the battle and falsifying events at least to the extent of saying that no ordinary human agency could overcome Andrea. *Nemesis* had to intervene to overthrow him; Balthazar couldn't kill him fairly, but had to take cowardly advantage in order to do so. We might accept Horatio's story without question if it were not different from the Spanish General's account and if Villuppo's lies in the preceding scene had not alerted us to the possibility of falsehood. And Horatio does not simply glorify Andrea at Balthazar's expense; a major portion of his story dwells on his own exploits and especially on his love of Andrea, his care for his friend's corpse, and his rescue of the scarf that must clearly have been Bel-imperia's token.

Bel-imperia gives Horatio her token, and he promises to serve her faithfully; then he leaves to serve her father's will by being a companion to Balthazar. Horatio's private feelings will be masked in his relations with Balthazar; and, although such courtly hypocrisy may be no more than routine "politeness" in the Spanish court, we might suspect that a person who can accept this falseness as routine could probably persuade himself to lie about the valor of an enemy and rival. But, if Horatio is possibly false to himself, to Bel-imperia, and to Balthazar, it may only be a matter of exaggerating certain aspects of the battle, an exaggeration inspired by a passion for an imperious beauty that destroys every person who is ruled by it.

Bel-imperia herself, however, may seem false in a more calculating way:

> Ay, go Horatio, leave me here alone,
> For solitude best fits my cheerless mood:
> Yet what avails to wail Andrea's death,
> From whence Horatio proves my second love?
> Had he not lov'd Andrea as he did,
> He could not sit in Bel-imperia's thoughts.
> But how can love find harbour in my breast,
> Till I revenge the death of my beloved?
> Yes, second love shall further my revenge.
> I'll love Horatio, my Andrea's friend,
> The more to spite the prince that wrought his end.
> And where Don Balthazar, that slew my love,
> Himself now pleads for favour at my hands,
> He shall in rigour of my just disdain
> Reap long repentance for his murd'rous deed:
> For what was't else but murd'rous cowardice,
> So many to oppress one valiant knight,
> Without respect of honour in the fight?
> And here he comes that murder'd my delight. (I.iv.58–76)

This soliloquy gives us our first insight into the character of Bel-imperia. Horatio may not have been consciously manipulating *her* emotions, but she certainly plans to use his love. As "solitude best fits my cheerless mood" reveals, she, like the other tragic characters, is isolated and imprisoned within this action that drives love into the service of hatred (58–59). She begins with the facts of her love for Horatio and her grief for Andrea (60–61). She does not doubt her new love, but she wants to justify it to herself in relation to her former love for Andrea (62–63). She evidently feels that she would be false to Andrea's love if she took a new lover without having first taken revenge on Balthazar (64–65). She does not want to frustrate her love, so the only solution is to *combine her love and her revenge* (66).

We are never to learn with certainty whether Bel-imperia intends to seek a *blood* revenge against Balthazar in which Horatio will be the murderous instrument. Revenge has told Andrea's ghost that he will see *her*, not Horatio, slay Balthazar, but Revenge does not say that this slaying will be directly in payment for the death of Andrea. Bel-imperia herself never mentions *killing* Balthazar except in connection with revenge for Horatio. In the soliloquy we are now studying, she seems to say that her affair with Horatio will itself be the instrument of her revenge: love itself will convey hatred (67–68). Although she says only that this love will "further" her revenge, she suggests no additional punishments for Balthazar except her "just disdain" which will make him "reap long repentance" (70–72). If she also plans to kill him, it will only be after a long period of emotional torment.

We might argue that the coldness of Bel-imperia's rationalization of love and hate was not *intended* by Kyd—that it is more a sign of his limited ability as a writer than of anything else. But it is not possible to talk about Kyd's intention apart from the evidence of the lines themselves, for there is no other evidence of his intent. If we like, we can suppose that this soliloquy is designed merely to give us information about Bel-imperia's plans without revealing her character, but there is no evidence to support such a view. The only assumption that makes sense for the interpretation of dramatic character is that, unless there is clear evidence to the contrary, every word anyone utters is at least indirectly an expression of his character, whether it also conveys information or not. The only exceptions to such a rule would be those cases in which there is some sign that a character has stepped out of his dramatic role to speak in behalf of the author or of the play. There is no sign that Bel-imperia steps out of her role to speak her soliloquy. As I have argued, she begins with the facts of two feelings, love and grief; and she proceeds to rationalize a connection between them and a third emotion, hatred. The fact that she discusses and does not express these emotions, even in the color of her language, suggests that her capacity for passion is limited by a certain coldness of heart and mind that links her with her brother Lorenzo and contrasts her with Hieronimo, Isabella, and the Viceroy. The contrast with the Viceroy should be immediately felt, since she echoes his lamentation in the preceding scene without conveying anything like the same intensity of feeling. After the Viceroy has thrown himself on the ground and wept for himself as a victim of Fortune he says: "Why wail I then, where's hope of no redress?/O yes, complaining makes my grief seem less" (I.iii.31–32). Bel-imperia feels no deep need to wail, perhaps because hope of redress makes her grief seem less: "Yet what avails to wail Andrea's death,/From whence Horatio proves my second love?" (I.iv.60–61).

The contrast-in-parallel between the Viceroy's grief and Bel-imperia's does not stop with this echo. As his emotional monologue was contrasted with a following passage of stichomythia involving three speakers, here Bel-imperia's rationalizing soliloquy is contrasted with a similar following passage. The Viceroy engaged in witless argument in stichomythia and was overwhelmed by Villuppo; Bel-imperia is a mistress of wit who easily outfences Balthazar. Balthazar is imprisoned by his "conceit," the thoughts and imaginings that love has made his mind derive from Petrarchan conventions. He is the play's most obvious prisoner, for his imprisonment by Spain and by love are both of a conventional sort that is easy to recognize. Bel-imperia is perhaps just as securely imprisoned in the solitude of her will, but her sort of imprisonment is internal and does not display itself in silly rhetoric or in Spanish sentries. The seeming self-command of her wit conceals her imprisonment even from herself. She thinks that she masters not only Balthazar but her own action, and she does not see the powers beyond her will that may really govern her.

Bel-imperia's disdain of Balthazar's words and his love is so great that she will not stay near him. In leaving the stage, she deliberately tortures him by dropping her handkerchief for Horatio to pick up. Her peculiar revenge for Andrea is well under way. Lorenzo steps in to comfort his distraught friend with the thought of remedies to cure Bel-imperia's mood, and courtly entertainments to distract Balthazar from his. Horatio makes the timely announcement that there will be a feast for the Portuguese

Ambassador, and Balthazar masks his private grief behind a public joy as he speaks to his father's emissary. Thus the first line of his speech is probably spoken only to himself; certainly it contrasts with the rest of what he says:

> AMB. Sad is our king, and Portingale laments,
> Supposing that Don Balthazar is slain.
> BAL. So am I slain, by beauty's tyranny.
> You see, my lord, how Balthazar is slain:
> I frolic with the Duke of Castile's son,
> Wrapp'd every hour in pleasures of the court,
> And grac'd with favours of his majesty. (119–25)

Balthazar is now figuratively, and will soon indeed be literally, slain by "beauty's tyranny," as good a translation of "Bel-imperia" as "beautiful and imperious." The possible ambiguity of Bel-imperia's name hints at the typical pattern of power in this play: the woman herself is an imperious beauty governing others, but the real power, her beauty, is not an expression of her character and it governs her just as surely as it governs the men.

The last four lines of Balthazar's speech ironically name a second agent of his death in the Spanish court—Lorenzo. Balthazar means only to jest in saying he is slain, but he is in truth killed through his friendship with Lorenzo in a courtly pleasure that is intended to be a mark of the King's favor.

The King invites everyone to partake of the banquet, including all those who are now or soon will be in conflict with one another. The banquet as a rite of brotherhood seals the breach between the nations that had forgotten they are interchangeable individuals: "Spain is Portugal,/And Portugal is Spain, we both are friends" (132–33). Ironically, however, peace between nations has not healed hostilities among individuals. Instead, it is breeding new hatred that will finally do greater injury to the two countries than the war could do. As in the battle, the fate of the nations depends on the actions of individuals. The King thinks that his power can control Bel-imperia with the help of her father (II.iii.41–50), but he is oblivious to the presence of higher powers like Revenge that control people through their passions.

During the feast, Hieronimo presents a dumbshow in three parts. This completes the action of the first act as a small parallel to the action of the entire play, foreshadowing as it does Hiero-

nimo's presentation of his play-within-the-play that celebrates
the joining of two individuals as this playlet celebrates the atone-
ment of two nations. For the second time in Act I, the King sees
a spectacle that pleases him but which Hieronimo must explain to
him (I.iv.138–40; cf. I.ii.110–16). But, despite his blindness, the
King feels perfectly well qualified to draw inferences from Hieronimo's dumbshow once Hieronimo has identified the historical
events it shadows forth as two English conquests of Portugal and
one of Spain.

The King's interpretation shows how people see what they want
to see in a play or an event. The King wants emblems of conquest
to help seal peace, so he reads them accordingly. His condescen-
sion to "little England" must have made Kyd's original audience
feel the partiality of his view. In a very real sense the responses to
the dumbshow sum up the relation of the contrasting accounts of
the battle in Act I to the play's more general concern for man's
tragic situation. Hieronimo's objective description of the dumbshow corresponds to the Spanish General's account of the battle,
and the King's following interpretations correspond to the stories
of Villuppo and Horatio, in which truth may be twisted or seen
only from the angle that serves the speaker's purpose.

The King accepts the first two parts of the dumbshow because
they dramatize conquests of Portugal, but the third part is a conquest of Spain, and the Portuguese Ambassador takes the opportunity to warn the Spanish not to crow too much. This warning
returns Spain and Portugal nearly to equality, and so the King
can accept the complete show as a *pleasing* device. The dumbshow can be regarded as a crude microcosm of the "mystery" of
tragic artistry: the individual events of a tragedy are painful to
behold, but the play brings them into pleasing relationships. Sim-
ilarly, the three conquests of the dumbshow were painful events
for Spain and Portugal, but their inter-relations as a dramatic unit
give pleasure to their royal audience.

The degree of a person's pleasure will depend on whether he
responds as an individual or as head or member of a group, and it
will also depend on his situation in other respects. As Spanish and
Portuguese officials and nationals, all the people in the courtly
audience find cause for pain in the separate events, but pleasure
in the events seen in relation to each other, provided they accept
the King's interpretation. But what does Horatio or Balthazar see

in the show in relation to his own private situation? What does Hieronimo see in the show in his special role as its creator? For the English theater audience, there is great pleasure in the separate parts of the show, but pain insofar as the Spanish enemy finds cause for hope in the whole—responses that are exactly opposite to those of the courtly audience within the play. And we must not forget the other audience on the stage: Andrea provides the point of view of the blindest member of the theater audience, requiring Revenge to explain all to those who cannot understand Act I as a whole any better than the Spanish King could fathom the microcosmic dumbshow without Hieronimo's help (I.v.1–9).

Andrea, who sees only the surface of events, the "pleasant sights," is oblivious to the way the love of Horatio and Belimperia is also a revenge against Balthazar that will cause him, in turn, to take revenge against Horatio. Revenge describes what is to happen as a transformation to be wrought in time, "ere we go from hence." If Andrea will be patient, he will see how love can *turn into* hate. This pattern of transformation is dramatized in Act II. Starting from this point of apparently amicable feasting, hostilities grow and come into the open. At the end of Act II Andrea will still be the man who has to have everything explained, but then at least he sees the hatred and its consequences and is only unable to see how the death of Horatio furthers his own cause. Imprisoned within his own emotions and desires, he cannot see how Revenge is working, but *we* note that at the end of Act I Revenge promises a general holocaust and not a justly discriminating punishment of crime:

I'll turn *their* friendship into fell despite,
Their love to mortal hate, *their* day to night,
Their hope into despair, *their* peace to war,
Their joys to pain, *their* bliss to misery. (Italics added I.v.5–9)

CHAPTER 4

Love and Death in the Garden

IN Act I we found that the outcome which Revenge has as his avowed goal, the slaying of Balthazar by Bel-imperia, is only implicit in Bel-imperia's use of her love of Horatio to punish Balthazar for killing Andrea. The relatively static expository function of the first act is expressed in both its form and its content: formally it repeats the same sort of scene again and again, and the content of each of its scenes is a judgment between rival claims. Thus, at the end of the act, issues have evolved and decisive judgments have been made, so that with the start of Act II Kyd is ready to develop the decisive plot action of the play.

Act II builds up to the climax of the "heart scene" of the play, scenes iv-v, which consummates the sequence of action begun in Act I and starts the sequence that will end in the slaying of Lorenzo and Balthazar by Hieronimo and Bel-imperia. This function of providing a point of balance between two phases of the action is expressed in the structure of parallels between scenes, just as parallels expressed the expository function of Act I: Act II contains five units of action, of which the first and the fifth parallel each other, as do the second and the fourth. The third scene is a point of concord and balance between these symmetrical sequences. Or we can simply say that the start of Hieronimo's revenge parallels the "revenge" of Balthazar out of which it grows.

Thus in Act II. i when Lorenzo and Balthazar learn of the love of Bel-imperia for Horatio, Balthazar's love makes him undertake revenge against his rival; and in scene v Hieronimo's love for his son makes him undertake revenge. In both scenes there is the hope that time is on the side of the lover-revenger (II. i. 1–7, II. 5. 57–59). In both scenes there is a natural progression from grieving for rejected or lost love to hatred and plans for revenge. In both scenes one of a suffering pair asks the other to stop lamenting and then proposes action:

> [BAL.]   Yet might she love me as her beauty's thrall,
>   Ay, but I fear she cannot love at all.
> LOR.   My lord, for my sake leave these ecstasies,
>   And doubt not but we'll find some remedy.
>   (II.i.27–30)
> [ISAB.] Time is the author both of truth and right,
>   And time will bring this treachery to light.
> HIER.   Meanwhile, good Isabella, cease thy plaints,
>   Or at the least dissemble them awhile:
>   So shall we sooner find the practice out.
>   (II.v.58–62)

The parallels between scenes i and v introduce a whole series of parallels and contrasts between Hieronimo and Lorenzo. Hieronimo, like Lorenzo, has been brought only indirectly into the conflict between Bel-imperia and Balthazar; and this faint parallel is later followed by stronger ones to suggest the similarity of the two men as *dissembling* revengers. Hieronimo tries to avoid using the devious means of the Machiavel, but Revenge is a Machiavel himself, and Hieronimo cannot escape his power.

Scenes ii and iv are parallel scenes in which Horatio and Bel-imperia meet as lovers, and in each case they talk of their love in metaphors of war, and in each they are spied upon. In scene ii they only *speak* of love in terms of war, and the response of their unseen enemies is to *speak* in a way that makes ironic point of the war, reversing the lovers' meanings:

> HOR. Dangers of war, and pleasures of our love.
> LOR. Dangers of death, but pleasures none at all. (II.ii.30–31)

In scene iv the lovers *act out* their love as a war climaxed in sexual "death," and the response of their enemies is to *act* in a way that reverses the lovers' meanings (II. iv. 46–55).

Scene iii, the point of balance in Act II, is, as we have observed, the one quiet moment in the midst of the conflicting passions of love and hate. The lovers and revengers want love to have issue in a "death" of some sort. The politicians still hope that hatred and death of the recent war will result in a peace sealed in love between Bel-imperia and Balthazar. The King, Castile, and the Portuguese Ambassador seem to move in an arena where there is some light. In the scenes of passion, on the other hand, there is a steady progression into the darkness promised by Revenge at the end of Act I (I. v. 5–7; II. i. 33–34; II. ii. 42–46, 56–57; II. iv. 1–5; II. v. 21–25).

Act II, Scene i

The structure of scene i signals the balance and the movement of Act II as a whole. Wolfgang Clemen has observed that Balthazar's two rhetorical speeches—one on his love, near the start of the scene, and the other on his hate for Horatio, at the end of the scene—are structural "corner-posts" to the action between.[1] The parallelism of these speeches stresses the change that takes place during the scene, for we feel the contrast between Balthazar's emotions all the more strongly when they are expressed within similar frames.

Lorenzo's opening speech links Act II with Act I by echoing Revenge's notion that if one is patient, he will see that changes will take place in time (I. v. 5–9, II. i. 1–8). Lorenzo's echo ironically reverses the direction of change that Revenge has demanded. Lorenzo, who as yet understands almost nothing, cannot see Revenge and Andrea; indeed, he is completely unaware that Bel-imperia is in love and is seeking revenge against Balthazar. Usually Lorenzo's is the most idiomatic and colloquial voice in the play, yet this speech on time and change is highly rhetorical. Kyd lifted these lines from Sonnet XLVII of Thomas Watson's *Hecatompathia,* and the appropriateness of the thought may have made him forget the inappropriateness for this character of the formal rhetoric. But perhaps we are to imagine that the formality of the speech is intended by Lorenzo to soothe Balthazar, as the content is clearly meant to do. Balthazar is almost in a frenzy as a result of Bel-imperia's rejection of his love, and the desperate conflict of his antitheses contrasts more strongly with the smoothness of Lorenzo's rhetorical parallels than it could with an informal style (19–28).

Balthazar, unable to understand why Bel-imperia has rejected him, begins by blaming her character, saying she is wilder than a beast and harder than a stone wall (9–10). Like Romeo in Act I of Shakespeare's play, Balthazar's conventional posturing as a lover shows that his love is really very shallow: he is in love with love and with Bel-imperia's beauty. Although he has hardly met the girl, he has a better grasp of her wild, hard nature than

he knows; and he instinctively hates her. At the outset, his love
is thus hollow—lacking a heart.

But Balthazar recoils from his real feelings: he "loves" her, so
she must be lovable and he should blame himself for her rejection
of his suit (11–12). As he searches for the fault in himself, he
becomes more and more emotional and rhetorical; and his true
feelings break through again (13–28). Balthazar concedes that
his appearance, his words, and his gifts to her might all be im-
proved; but, when he turns from these external matters to his
character, he can do nothing but praise himself and find reasons
why she should love him. He concludes that she is as hard as he
first suggested, so hard that "she cannot love at all" (28).

But Balthazar has little real understanding of himself, of Bel-
imperia, or, as events unfold, of Lorenzo. Because of his passion,
Balthazar is hardly able to think at all; his mind zigzags swiftly
between the poles of antitheses as it moves in a larger, slower
zigzag from blaming Bel-imperia to blaming himself and back
to blaming her again. Lorenzo, however, is unemotional and
purposeful; and he progresses directly from a definition of their
problem to what he takes to be its logical solution:

> My lord, for my sake leave these ecstasies,
> And doubt not but we'll find some remedy:
> Some cause there is that lets you not be lov'd:
> First that must needs be known and then remov'd.
> What if my sister love some other knight?
> BAL. My summer's day will turn to winter's night.
>
> (29–34)

Lorenzo is well aware of the futility and weakness of Balthazar's emotional ecstacies, but he has no understanding of the
futility and weakness of his own thinking. Having no passion of
his own, he is incapable of understanding the peculiar pattern
of emotions like love. His vision of reality is entirely limited to
a perception of cause and effect relationships conceived in bru-
tally physical and simple terms: there is a *cause* that keeps Bel-
imperia from loving Balthazar; therefore, find out the cause,
remove it, and all will be well. Hypothesis number one is "What
if my sister love some other knight?" The implied course of action: if they find out who her lover is and kill him, then Bel-

imperia will love Balthazar. Now this logic is what Lorenzo actually relies on in killing Horatio. When we reduce it to its hypothetical syllogism, as I have just done, we can immediately see that Lorenzo's failure to take the psychology of love into account is absurd. He is entirely deaf to Balthazar's reply to his question. In the higher logic of rhyme and love, "other knight" quite simply and hopelessly implies "winter's night."

Lorenzo thinks people can be motivated by external forces very much as puppets are. He sees humans as isolated individuals who can be governed by appeals to interests so selfish that a person will care only about the fact of his own love and not care what individual responds to that love: Bel-imperia will love Balthazar if they kill Horatio. Lorenzo uses three strings to move people like puppets: persuasive words, threats of violence, and the temptation of worldly riches and power (108–9). His idea that a smooth story and the advantages of a marriage with Balthazar will win Bel-imperia after Horatio is dead is absurd; but his faith in such motivators of others is confirmed by success with Pedringano, Bel-imperia's trusted servant.

Lorenzo succeeds with Pedringano because Pedringano is as incapable of love and as narrowly selfish as he is himself. He goes to work on Pedringano in very direct fashion, reminding him that he saved him from punishment in the affair of Andrea and then offering him rewards if he will tell who Bel-imperia now loves. Pedringano, trying to be true to his mistress, says he is no longer in her confidence. When Lorenzo draws his sword and threatens to kill if Pedringano does not talk, all the strings on his puppet have been yanked: ". . . fear shall force what friendship cannot win./ . . . Yet speak the truth and I will guerdon thee,/ And shield thee from whatever can ensue" (68, 72–73).

Pedringano then names Horatio as the new lover, and the coldly logical and mechanical Lorenzo asks how he knows. After Pedringano has described the letters Bel-imperia sent to Horatio, Lorenzo uses force again, threatening to kill him if his story is false or if he betrays the fact that he has told it. Pedringano tries to make it sound as if the desire to serve Lorenzo, rather than force and fear, has moved him; he hopes that Lorenzo will trust him and not forget to offer rewards rather than threats on future occasions (94–97). Lorenzo assigns Pedringano the additional duty of reporting the lovers' meetings, promising that he will "find that I am liberal . . . be therefore wise and fail me not" (102–4).

This perversion of equating selfish cunning with wisdom was a notion familiar to the Elizabethans from diatribes against it in the Bible, sermons, and morality plays, and in attacks on Machiavelli. "Devil" Lorenzo has tempted and coerced poor Pedringano into becoming Mr. Worldly-Wiseman. There has even been a blasphemous ritual that inverts truth and justice to seal the damnation of Pedringano's soul (87–93). Pedringano has sold his soul under such great duress that, ironically, his devil-master can scarcely be expected to trust him and reward him as promised. As we see in different terms and on a far grander scale in Marlowe's *Doctor Faustus*, the circumstances of bargaining with the devil deny the possibility of enjoying the reward for which a man sells his soul: the pains of damnation begin in this life; they do not wait any twenty-four years until one goes to hell.

Pedringano departs, and Lorenzo summarizes his triumphant strategy: "Where words prevail not, violence prevails:/But gold doth more than either of them both" (108–9). Balthazar's words in reply are as emotional as Lorenzo's were cold, and his analysis of his predicament is very illuminating. He sees that Lorenzo's strategy will fail, that "she'll fly me if I take revenge" (115); but his love forces him to take revenge: "Yet must I take revenge or die myself,/For love resisted grows impatient" (116–17). Although Balthazar's reason shows him the truth, his passions overwhelm his reason, and he feels he *must* kill Horatio. The relation of love and hate is complex: Balthazar loves Bel-imperia, but she loves Horatio and hates Balthazar. Her love of Horatio makes Balthazar hate him. Thus Balthazar's passionate love itself makes him *increase* her hatred for him by killing her lover. If Balthazar does not kill Horatio, he will himself be killed by the power of his own love. Bel-imperia's love for Andrea and Balthazar's for her are now hateful, destructive forces partly because they have been *frustrated*. One of Kyd's major interests in this play is to study the power of frustration to pervert both love and the quest for justice into ugly forms.

After resolving to kill Horatio, Balthazar speaks of his double conquest by his rival: first, by force in battle; second, by guileful words in love (118–29). The rhetoric stresses the parallel of love and war, then concludes in a way that suggests a parallel between Pedringano and Balthazar: "Thus hath he ta'en my body by his force,/And now by sleight would captivate my soul" (130–31). The threat of violence wins Balthazar's and Pedringano's bodies to obedience, and then "pleasing words" conquer their spirits (108, 125). However, the pleasing words of Horatio, that Balthazar says conquer him, conquer only Bel-imperia directly. Balthazar does not realize that the pleasing words that govern him come from the same man whose words have governed Pedringano. Earlier in the speech, as I have noted, Balthazar saw that "she'll fly me if I take revenge," but now he accepts Lorenzo's idea that killing Horatio is the way to win Bel-imperia: "in his fall I'll tempt the destinies,/And either lose my life, or win my love" (132–33). In his passion, Balthazar has lost sight of the true human relations and emotions concerned and has come to think of Horatio as a sort of super- or sub-human force of destiny (118, 132). With the tragic blindness typical of the people in the play, he fails to see Revenge as the force of destiny; and he also fails to see a fellow human as one like himself. Revenge knows that if he kills Horatio he dooms himself and loses his love even more irretrievably than he has already.

Lorenzo, despite his calm, is even blinder than Balthazar; the idea that killing Horatio will hurt Balthazar's chances with Bel-imperia does not even occur to him. Balthazar should simply submit himself to Lorenzo's government and all will be well (135). The dialogue between these two in the first part of the scene reached a climax in the rhymes expressing the emotional illogic of Lorenzo's strategy of removing a lover to generate love and the emotional logic of Balthazar's response that "other knight" means "winter's night." This second, balancing dialogue concludes with Lorenzo's reiteration of the emotional illogic of his strategy, again with a rhyme that negates his hope; but now Balthazar's despair is so great that he acquiesces in his friend's plan:

> Lor. Let's go my lord, your staying stays revenge.
> Do you but follow me and gain your love:
> Her favour must be won by his remove. (134–36)

Act II, Scene ii

This scene, in which Horatio and Bel-imperia meet to talk of their love, has a beautifully articulated structure. Since the subject is love, there might not be any dramatic conflict at all. But both the cause and the effect of this love is violence, and this is suggested by their talk of love in terms of war. The violent potential of that talk is made clear only in the dialogue between the spying Balthazar and Lorenzo that the lovers do not hear. The conflict is thus entirely indirect, allowing for a more arbitrary formality in the arrangement of the dialogue than is usual. Another element of formality is in the greater than usual use of rhyme in this scene.

The scene begins with Horatio asking Bel-imperia why she seems unhappy in the midst of their happy love-talk. We have come upon them in the course of their wooing, much as Lorenzo and Balthazar are to do six lines later. (The lovers, who want to be alone, must play out their affair before no fewer than three audiences.) It is hard to gauge how innocent Horatio is when he asks Bel-imperia about her unhappiness. In describing their love "blandishments," he puts his finger directly upon the gap in their relations that is causing her "languishments." "Looks and words," he says, are "Two chief contents, where more cannot be had" (II. ii. 3–4). More can be had, of course, and Bel-imperia immediately makes it plain that she wants more—the physical possession of his love. Bel-imperia's rhymes indicate the meaning she sees in their love. She thinks of the past as a wild storm, of their love as a quiet haven or as the ordered harmonies of "Cupid's quire" (16). She thus contrasts future "joy" and past "annoy," then allows the contrasting elements to conflict with one another by alternating them in the rhyme-sequence of "port"—"toss'd"—"resort"—"lost," and concludes with the lover's harmonizing of "quire"—"desire" (10–17).

Bel-imperia pins her hopes on the notion that "pleasure follows pain, and bliss annoy," but Philip Edwards' note on this line tells us that the opposite idea is proverbial. He quotes Watson's *Teares of Fancie*: "Pleasure doubleth paine and blisse annoy." The irony is a simple one—if Bel-imperia could see Lorenzo and Balthazar spying on her, she would know that old proverbs cannot be beaten:

> BAL. O sleep mine eyes, see not my love profan'd,
> Be deaf my ears, hear not my discontent,
> Die heart, another joys what thou deserv'st.

LOR. Watch still mine eyes, to see this love disjoin'd,
          Hear still mine ears, to hear them both lament,
          Live heart, to joy at fond Horatio's fall. (18–23)

Balthazar's passion continues to blind, deafen, and destroy him.
As Lorenzo opens his eyes wide to pursue a course that will finally
kill him, his only emotion is his intense anticipation of sadistic
pleasure in destroying relations between others. Balthazar feels
himself cut off from his proper relations to others; Lorenzo denies
his real relation to his sister in his wish to hear her lament. We
might imagine that their responses correspond roughly to those
of Andrea and Revenge. Andrea might well feel jealous of both
Balthazar and Horatio, as Balthazar does of Horatio; and Revenge
almost certainly whispers "amen" to Lorenzo's speech, adding
the death of Lorenzo himself to his sadistic anticipation as Andrea adds Balthazar to his jealousy.

The pattern of the scene as a whole should now be clear. The
lovers think their love is carrying them from storm and pain to
resort, quire, and pleasure. A counter-movement is begun by
Lorenzo and Balthazar in lines 18–23, and then the two directions
of movement clash head-on in the stichomythia. Following this,
the lovers themselves implicitly (and ironically) acknowledge
that they move not from storm to calm but from "dangers" to
"war" (32–37). Thus in many of Bel-imperia's lines in this later
part of the scene the movement is from fair words, looks, lines,
or kisses to cross and countercheck. This direction is summed up
in the way Bel-imperia selects the field for their "warring peace,
or peaceful war": "Then be thy father's pleasant bower the
field,/Where first we vow'd a mutual amity" (42–43). The bower
was *first* the place where they vowed mutual amity; now it will
be "the field/Where trial of this war shall first be made" (39–40).
After Bel-imperia appoints the field of love-war, however, her
closing speech returns to the language of peace and harmony,
balancing her speech near the start of the scene and even echoing her earlier mention of "Cupid's quire" in talk of nightingales
who will carol the lovers to sleep. Danger, she and Horatio think,
lurks only in the court. The garden is to be a place where "honey
sweet, and honourable love" can be consummated in all innocence and safety (53). What is really the situation can be seen
at a glance if we scan the four rhymes that close the scene. Lov-

ers leave "father's sight" for their "delight," but "jealous despite"
sends one of them to "eternal night."

Act II, Scene iii

The Spanish King's political scheme for bringing Bel-imperia
and Balthazar together neglects the psychology of passion in its
manipulation of human actions, although not nearly as much as
Lorenzo's murderous scheme does. Bel-imperia's marriage to Balthazar will unite Spain and Portugal and is therefore to be desired, so the puppeteer pulls the strings to make her throw her
arms around the man and to make the Portuguese Viceroy ap-
prove the match. The Duke of Castile threatens to coerce his
daughter, and the King promises kingdoms for Balthazar's de-
scendants to rule (II.iii.8, 20–21). The sum of the King's view is
that "Young virgins must be ruled by their friends" (43).

The King and Bel-imperia's father are worried about her partly
because they have some understanding of the nature of woman.
They vaguely realize that Bel-imperia may be "froward" (6).
Contrasting with their view of her as perverse and *from*-ward is
their conception of Horatio as a man whose "forwardness deserves reward" (35). Without minimizing Horatio's courageous
"forwardness" in battle, we can observe that the use of these
terms oversimplifies the contrast between the two lovers. Horatio
is *for*ward as a bold warrior, courtier, and lover. Bel-imperia
seems to be *fro*ward in the sense of *coy,* but it is ironic that her
father thinks she acts coy to conceal her love for Balthazar, when
actually it is to conceal her hate for him (3–4). Bel-imperia is
really a very *for*ward young woman where her own will and
desire move her to be. The Duke talks like a typical puppeteer-
father. *His* will is direct and proper; and, if his child's will is
independent of his, he can only see this from his own point of
view and call her coy, froward, and perverse.

The promise of the Duke to coerce his daughter if necessary is
enough to convince the King that it is safe to set his hopes of lasting peace on the wedding of Bel-imperia and Balthazar. Yet the
King knows full well that Bel-imperia has still to be won over, and
the scene ends as it began with concern for the need to control
her will. The Duke's speech at the start of the scene reflected
his relation to her as a father-puppeteer trying to conceal from
his audience the fact that his puppet is out of his control. The

King's speech at the end of the scene, in contrast, takes a more direct and realistic view, acknowledging that Bel-imperia has a will of her own and must be won from it (41–43).

There is great irony in the placing of this scene between two scenes showing Bel-imperia's love for Horatio. While the King and her father talk of her wedding to Balthazar, she and Horatio are planning an act of love that will kill Spain and Portugal's hopes. But the will of Bel-imperia's brother also crosses their father's and the King's hopes, for Lorenzo's strategy of joining one set of lovers by "disjoining" another can achieve only the "disjoining" and must deny all hopes of a royal wedding.

Act II, Scene iv

In Act II.ii, Bel-imperia told Horatio that her heart has been long tossed in a storm of conflicting hopes and fears and that she hopes to find in his love a secure resting place where fears may be forgotten and hopes fulfilled. In scene iv they meet in his father's arbor to consummate their hopes of love, but Bel-imperia finds that it is very difficult to shed her fears before entering the "safe" haven. Since this love is for Bel-imperia an expression of her hatred of Balthazar, thoughts of violence are inevitable. And for the logic of the inner reality of the situation it is also inevitable that the sexual climax or "death" of this love should be cut short by a literal death of the lovers. Horatio is to die indeed in the consummation of his love, and the deaths of both Balthazar and Bel-imperia are certain once Horatio is dead.

The intensity of the scene builds gradually to its climax of love and violence. In the first twenty-three lines the lovers gradually shed their fears on entry into the supposedly secure haven of the bower. For the next fourteen lines they exchange rhymed couplets of conventionally ritualized amatory talk. With the last of these couplets they begin their physical intimacy, and the dialogue reaches the verbal intimacy of stichomythia as they act out the wars of love. Following the quick fire of the first "darted" kisses, the dialogue passes back into the blissful harmony of rhymed couplets as the lovers relax in the false security of a sensuous embrace in which they pass toward the bliss and enervation of sexual death. At this very moment of relaxed bliss the murderers knife in upon their harmony of rhyming love with the sharp discords of verbal cacaphony and physical violence.

The ambiguity of the love of Bel-imperia and Horatio is implied in the ambiguity of the darkness of the scene (II.iv.1–5, 14–21). Although Horatio says darkness favors their hope for security in love, we know it can also be a fearful omen and a cloak for murderers. Horatio's view is entirely one-sided because he is caught up in the excitement of his love, and his sanguinary view of night and of the favor of Fortune are calculated by Kyd to make us shiver with Bel-imperia as we hear it. If he says "in darkness pleasures may be done," we reply with an ironic reversal of his hope, partly because we are influenced by the earlier scene in which Lorenzo and Balthazar made ironic comments as an audience of sorts. An appropriate reply might be the words of Hieronimo a little later when he finds his son's body: "O heavens, why made you night to cover sin?/By day this deed of darkness had not been" (II.v.24–25).

Between Horatio's two speeches trying to convince Bel-imperia that darkness is a favorable omen, the lovers dispatch Pedringano to guard the gate. With the romantic abandon typical of the lover, Horatio is very much concerned with the relation of his love to the sun, the moon, the stars, darkness, and Fortune; but he has only a perfunctory interest in its relation to other humans. Bel-imperia assures him that Pedringano is "as trusty as my second self," and that is all there is to it (II.iv.9). To Horatio, Pedringano is little more than an object that, with these words from Bel-imperia, may be counted on to act as a mechanical lock to secure the gate.

Bel-imperia knows Pedringano better, speaking as though she thinks of him as a fellow human on her own level—as a form of herself and not as a puppet or an object. However, the expression "trusty as my second self" is really only a form of speech for Bel-imperia, for if she stopped to think she would remember that she herself is not entirely to be trusted by others. She is deceiving her father in her relations with Horatio, as she had before deceived him with Andrea. She is false to Balthazar by concealing her hate in coy rejection of his suit. And most of all, perhaps, she is false to Horatio, using her affair with him as part of her revenge against Balthazar, yet never telling him so as far as we can see. Her secrecy is no more than tit for tat, for, as we have seen, Horatio's love may also be tainted by falseness. Nevertheless, Horatio has been conquered by Bel-imperia's imperious beauty and is at least

infatuated with her, as she must be with him. It might be argued
that Horatio's reassurance of Bel-imperia in this scene is part of a
calculating effort to possess her, but I think he convinces himself
of their safety and is much less concerned about the lock on the
gate than he would be if he were not genuinely blinded by passion.

Horatio wins Bel-imperia's confidence, and they sit in the easy
security of the arbor's "leavy bowers." They sense other presences
and even jealous eyes in the dark about them, but not the real
dangers that lurk:

> HOR. The more thou sit'st within these leavy bowers,
>   The more will Flora deck it with her flowers.
> BEL. Ay, but if Flora spy Horatio here,
>   Her jealous eye will think I sit too near.
> HOR. Hark, madam, how the birds record by night,
>   For joy that Bel-imperia sits in sight.
> BEL. No, Cupid counterfeits the nightingale,
>   To frame sweet music to Horatio's tale.
> HOR. If Cupid sing, then Venus is not far:
>   Ay, thou art Venus or some fairer star.
> BEL. If I be Venus thou must needs be Mars,
>   And where Mars reigneth there must needs be wars.
>   (24–35)

The actual flowers remind them of the "jealous eye" of Flora.
From this ominous love conceit the actual birds they hear lead
them to people the dark with more such imaginary, mythic presences. Imagined birdsong in their earlier love scene meant "Cupid's quire," so here real birdsong leads to thoughts of Cupid,
thence to his mother, Venus, and thence to Venus' lover, Mars.
This chain of relationship has led ominously from the secure
pleasure and ease of lovers enjoying a leafy bower and the harmony of birdsong to talk of war as "death" approaches. In the
action of the scene Mars will indeed reign in violence in only a
few moments, and the language of the scene is also moving toward his reign through its chain of imaginative associations from
harmony to warlike conflict.

The lovers are now so much entranced with each other and the
sexual acting-out of their imaginings that they are oblivious to
any darker potentialities of their language or actions:

HOR. Then thus begin our wars: put forth thy hand,
  That it may combat with my ruder hand.
BEL. Set forth thy foot to try the push of mine.
HOR. But first my looks shall combat against thine.
BEL. Then ward thyself, I dart this kiss at thee.
HOR. Thus I retort the dart thou threw'st at me.
BEL. Nay then, to gain the glory of the field,
  My twining arms shall yoke and make thee yield.
HOR. Nay then, my arms are large and strong withal:
  Thus elms by vines are compass'd till they fall.
BEL. O let me go, for in my troubled eyes
  Now may'st thou read that life in passion dies.
HOR. O stay awhile and I will die with thee,
  So shalt thou yield and yet have conquer'd me.
BEL. Who's there? Pedringano! We are betray'd!
  Enter LORENZO, BALTHAZAR, SERBERINE, PEDRIN-
  GANO, *disguised.* (36–50)

Every metaphor in this passage implies that their love is destructive. This element is the one principle of unity in these lines, for the metaphors are not consistently those of war. The sexual contact of hand and foot and mouth is said to be a war, but the love embrace is figured forth as one plant destroying another. The image of the vine climbing up to choke the elm may imply that Horatio is an ambitious parasite; and, although it is of course not so intended by Horatio, an Elizabethan audience might feel the irony because proverbially the vine supports the tree and does not pull it down, as Philip Edwards observes in his note on the passage.

Bel-imperia's eyes are "troubled"; and, as Shakespeare writes in *The Taming of the Shrew,* "A woman moved is like a fountain troubled" (V.ii.142). Her passion fully aroused, she is now about to "die." At the same time the lines carry a second meaning. Her eyes ought to be not only *murky* with passion, but *disturbed* with fear and concern for what she is doing because it is deeply true that "life in passion dies." Bel-imperia intends some of this second meaning, for she cries "O let me go"; but Horatio is thinking only of consummation, and his reply delights in the sexual paradox of surrender and conquest, die and die, without any misgivings at all.

Then the scene is violently transformed. Portentous, symbolic, ritualized sensual dialogue gives way to the terrible drama of character at the moment of death. This murder is the only one in the play in which the victim knows that he is being killed long enough to respond, and it is the only murder in which the emotions of the participants are felt with dramatic immediacy. The immediacy is important, for this is the "heart scene" of the play to which all that has gone before has led and from which all that comes after issues forth. Thus the responses of the characters at this awful moment are what go on to develop the balance of the play. The image of death itself, with all its horror, is also dwelt upon to intensify its significance as a picture to hold in the mind through all that follows:

LOR. My lord, away with her, take her aside.
　　　O sir, forbear, your valour is already tried.
　　　Quickly despatch, my masters. *They hang him in the Arbour.*

HOR. What, will you murder me?
LOR. Ay, thus, and thus, these are the fruits of love. *They stab him.*

BEL. O save his life and let me die for him!
　　　O save him brother, save him Balthazar:
　　　I lov'd Horatio but he lov'd not me.
BAL. But Balthazar loves Bel-imperia.
LOR. Although his life were still ambitious proud,
　　　Yet is he at the highest now he is dead.
BEL. Murder! murder! Help, Hieronimo, help!
LOR. Come stop her mouth, away with her. (51–63)

Lorenzo is unutterably his businesslike self in ordering Balthazar and his henchmen about and in enjoying the cruel irony of his gibe at Horatio's futile resistance. Horatio's hopeless "What, will you murder me?" is a fine piece of verisimilitude that captures the surprise, the shock, and, above all, that sheer disbelief in death that is so natural when a man is taken in the midst of life. Lorenzo insists on his ironic, exulting view of murder by calling the stabs that kill Horatio the "fruits of love." This completes the pun on "die," of course, but it may also imply that Lorenzo's nature is so demonic and perverted that sadistic stabs are the only kind of sexual passion he is capable of feeling.

Bel-imperia's thoughts are all to save Horatio. She turns desperately from offering herself as victim to appealing to Lorenzo and then to Balthazar. In her horror and grief, she even resorts to denying Horatio's love for her; but she reveals the only thing that matters to Balthazar, that she loved Horatio. The pathetic Balthazar can only respond, with despair to match hers, that he loves her. How well his deeds have expressed his feelings! Lorenzo gives us a further clue to his own motives when he ironically observes that Horatio was "ambitious proud" but has risen only in a noose. To Balthazar, Horatio was a rival in war and in love; to Lorenzo, he was a rival in the capture of Balthazar and consequently in honor and pride before the Spanish court. Horatio made Lorenzo feel inferior. Lorenzo could not defeat his will or control his acts, and his envy made him hate and destroy. Lorenzo's friends must all be emotional weaklings like Balthazar, his servants venal like Pedringano.

Act II, Scene v

Scene iv closes upon Bel-imperia's helpless outcries and Lorenzo's final cold command to stop her mouth and take her away. The four murderers drag Bel-imperia off, and the body of Horatio is left swinging in the darkness of the once-more quiet arbor. Immediately, Hieronimo enters in his nightshirt; and we have the most important and memorable of all the responses to Horatio's death—the moment of ultimate terror as a proud and loving father discovers the mutilated corpse of his only son. This moment is the one that lives in the mind of the audience as the emotional source of the following action. We know that it lived in the mind of its original Elizabethan audiences, for in the anonymous additions to the play, first printed in 1602, Hieronimo is made to re-create the scene verbally after having lived through it here; and in the quarto edition of 1615 the scene is depicted on the title page.

Most of the characters of *The Spanish Tragedy* seek revenge—Revenge himself, Andrea, Horatio, Bel-imperia, Lorenzo, Balthazar, the Viceroy—but the character of "the revenger" as he was to pass into the mainstream of Elizabethan drama is set forth in detail only in Hieronimo. So far in the play we know this man only as a loyal subject and a reasonable judge who is especially concerned that justice should be done to the true merit of his son. In scene v we are suddenly given a full view of his deeper emo-

tions. Kyd unfolds action and character gradually as the scene
develops so that we can see many aspects of Hieronimo's nature.
At first Hieronimo responds to fearful nocturnal outcries and to
the discovery of a dead body, but he does not recognize the body
as Horatio's (II.v.1–12). Here he shows his regard for the need
of others and for the problem of guilt. In the next part of the
scene he discovers that the body is Horatio's, and he is overwhelmed by a combination of grief, moral outrage, and horror
(13–33). Then he is joined by his wife, Isabella; and he lets her
weep and lament, while he turns to thoughts of revenge (34–65).
In the last part of the scene he responds to the total situation in a
ritualized summation spoken in Latin: his despairing grief makes
him want to commit suicide, but he resolves to stay alive until
he has avenged his son (66–80). These two related desires, for
suicide and for revenge, for self-destruction and for destruction of
others, are to be at the heart of all his thoughts, emotions, motives, and deeds for the duration of the play.

Something about Bel-imperia's outcry strikes the fear of a life-
time to the heart of Hieronimo, yet he comes because he feels he
must rescue her. We know why he feels the unaccustomed fear,
and we can only admire his courage and at the same time suffer
a fear of our own for what he will discover. Among his first words
on finding the body is one line that may have special significance.
The murderers have left the body hanging "in my bower, to lay
the guilt on me" (11). This statement recalls Hieronimo's background as a judge and also introduces in a subtle way the question of his guilt—a question that is a major concern for the balance of the play as he turns to blood revenge.

When he has cut the body down and recognized it as Horatio's,
Hieronimo speaks a long rhetorical lament. His speech as he entered and discovered the body moved from point to point on a
series of "ands" and "buts" that followed his emotions and
thoughts as events unfolded. Now he dwells on a single event,
the murder of Horatio, and rhetorical parallelism expresses the
emotional recurrence of this event in his lament:

> These garments that he wears I oft have seen—
> Alas, it is Horatio my sweet son!
> O no, but he that whilom was my son.
> O was it thou that call'dst me from my bed?

O speak, if any spark of life remain:
I am thy father. Who hath slain my son?
What savage monster, not of human kind,
Hath here been glutted with thy harmless blood,
And left thy bloody corpse dishonour'd here,
For me amidst this dark and deathful shades
To drown thee with an ocean of my tears?
O heavens, why made you night to cover sin?
By day this deed of darkness had not been.
O earth, why didst thou not in time devour
The vild profaner of this sacred bower?
O poor Horatio, what hadst thou misdone,
To leese thy life ere life was new begun?
O wicked butcher, whatso'er thou wert,
How could thou strangle virtue and desert?
Ay me most wretched, that have lost my joy,
In leesing my Horatio, my sweet boy! (13–33)

Moody Prior points out that this speech begins and closes formally although it has a fairly informal middle section, and he finds
the mixing of styles ineffective in this instance.[2] But the contrast
of the different parts of the speech is greater on the printed
page than it would be when delivered on the stage. The repetition of "O" is simply emotional at the start of the speech.
Since the "O"s do not introduce rhetorically parallel lines, they
should not be spoken in a way to imply a formal structure. The
repetition of "O" and "Ay" in the last part of the speech does
introduce parallel rhetorical questions, and Kyd has reinforced
the rhetoric by making each unit a rhymed couplet. Yet the main
effect even here is Hieronimo's passion. The couplets are not to be
spoken with measured stress on meter, rhyme, and rhetoric. The
outbursts of "O heavens" and so on must be spoken as separate
cries of passion, followed only after a pause by the rest of the
couplet. And there should be pauses between the couplets. In
this way the parallel units will be felt as parallel expressions of
emotion, and the rhetoric will be felt only enough to establish the
parallels and the movement of thought and emotion in the passage.

From the initial "Alas" to the final "Ay me" the movement of the
speech is toward progressively more articulate and less immediate
grief. At first there is the terror of recognition, and then the tragic
pathos of "O no, but he that whilom was my son" in which Kyd

may suggest that death has destroyed a relationship of love so that love is no longer really relevant to Horatio. The speech goes on to explore what now remains. Once more Hieronimo tries to communicate with his son, pathetically identifying himself to the corpse as its father. But there is no response, and Hieronimo's thwarted love is turned to hate of the murderers. First he cries out "Who hath slain my son?"; and, as his passion mounts, he expands this into a rhetorical question five lines long. The murderers are monsters, Horatio was harmless and has been dishonored, and he, Hieronimo, has been left with a burden of grief (19–23). The climax is in the return of passion to himself as a pitiful sufferer. There is a potentially dangerous if poignant element of self-pity in all grief of this kind: Horatio is dead and cannot appreciate Hieronimo's feelings, but the murderers and Hieronimo can still suffer. The climactic image in this rhetorical question speaks of Hieronimo's need to "drown thee with an ocean of my tears." This image is echoed and carried further a little later when Isabella cries "O gush out, tears, fountains and floods of tears," and again in the opening lines of Hieronimo's next scene, when he says "O eyes, no eyes, but fountains fraught with tears" .(II.v.43, III.ii.1). All these passages may be related to Bel-imperia's "In my troubled eyes/Now may'st thou read that life in passion dies" (II.iv.46–47). Before life dies in passion, vision or judgment has been lost. The image of eyes as no longer eyes because they are full of tears expresses this idea with power.

After the climax in the "ocean of tears," with its hint that Hieronimo's passionately blind grief may destroy—drown—its object, the last part of the speech develops a similar progression of emotion, this time from a general concern for the evil that has been done to a self-pitying grief that must move our sympathies despite our awareness that it may lead to evil. The first of the five couplets picks up the notion of dark as "deathful" (l. 22) and asks why God made night to "cover sin." Murder is a "deed of darkness" in the next line, and it could not have happened in daylight. But did not the deed happen when and where it did because of what Horatio wanted to do under cover of dark, and might not Elizabethans think of his deed as a sin, even though they might think only of the murder as a deed of darkness? As Hieronimo said in line 12, the bower "was made for pleasure, not for death." Who first brought a form of "death" and war to it? Are we not to think of Horatio as bearing at least a little of the taint of being "The

vild profaner of this sacred bower?" In part, then, these lines have
been implicitly leading up to the next question, "O poor Horatio,
what hadst thou misdone . . . ?"

For Hieronimo, however, this is a rhetorical question in the
sense that he means to imply the answer that Horatio has done
nothing to deserve death. The next question contains this answer
when it calls the murderers butchers who attacked "virtue" and
"desert." Thus Hieronimo appears to be seeking understanding
of what has happened, but his questions become assertions when
they are read in sequence. He assumes that his son was innocent
and deserving and that he has been murdered without cause, and
his questions are desperate efforts to understand in emotional
terms how the powers that be could have allowed such a horror
to occur. Why was there not a miracle? How could men of flesh
and blood be so monstrous as to violate the laws of God and nature
and kill one of their own kind? The most terrible thing about
such a loss is the injustice of it: How could it happen? and why
did it have to happen? and, finally, to *me?* Once more the emotion
has returned from the lost one to the individual who lives to suffer
the pain of loss. Hieronimo is indeed the "most wretched," and
must find something to do with his passions or drown in the tears
of his own grief and self-pity.

Isabella now enters to take over the lamentation while Hieronimo begins to find an outlet for his emotions in thoughts of revenge (36–41). In lines 42–45 she reproduces in little the long lament of Hieronimo which we have just studied, echoing his image
of tears. Kyd magnifies this image into a great storm, perhaps to
make up for the brevity of her speech. Hieronimo pays a last loving tribute to his son, then "stays" or holds back tears and words of
grief for thoughts of hate and blood revenge (46–56). Hieronimo
will keep the bloody handkerchief and the body as constant re-
minders to goad him on to his revenge, and Isabella has faith that
they will be able to see the treacherous murderers in God's good
time (57–59). She says "the heavens are just," and does not seem
to feel that she and Hieronimo will need to bring the criminals to
light themselves.

In contrast, Hieronimo in his lament has questioned the justice of the heavens (24–27). He is determined to take revenge,
and in the passion of his grief he has not stopped to ask himself
whether revenge will be just and in accord with the will of the
heavens. At this moment, revenge is simply a necessity to his emo-

tional state of mingled love, hate, and self-pitying despair. And
the work of bringing the murderers to light is not to be left to
heaven and time (60–63). As the dirge that follows also makes
clear, Hieronimo himself must be active in bringing the killers
to light and taking revenge; otherwise, his emotional energies
would force him to destroy himself. Hieronimo's posture as he
speaks his Latin dirge reflects his complex emotions. He and Isabella support Horatio's body between them, but also Hieronimo
places a sword against his breast in readiness to slay himself. At
the end of the dirge, however, he has resolved to live at least until
he gets his revenge, and so he throws the sword aside and bears
Horatio's body away.

The Latin dirge profoundly reveals the suicide impulse that
underlies the motivation of Hieronimo's revenge. Throughout the
world he will seek drugs and poisons that bring oblivion to the
mind and heart, even unto death, in order to kill all feeling. His
passion is too great to live with; his pain of loss can be comforted
only by joining the lost one in death. But he will not die a hasty
death, since there would then be no revenge. Instead, he is to die
the slow death of becoming a revenger, a role in which his original being as judge and as father is denied and destroyed even as
he destroys his enemies. The tempting emotional perversity of revenge is felt in Hieronimo's expectation of joy in sorrow:

> Seest thou those wounds that yet are bleeding fresh?
> I'll not entomb them till I have reveng'd:
> Then will I joy amidst my discontent,
> Till then my sorrow never shall be spent. (53–56)

Act II, Scene vi

In scene vi Andrea continues to play his assigned role as the
least perceptive member of Kyd's audience. He was unhappy at
the end of Act I because his enemy was happy. Now things have
gone from bad to worse and he is sad because only his friends
are sad. But Revenge asks him to wait patiently for the time to
pass that will bring the season to harvest. Isabella thinks time will
bring about the just action of the heavens against the murderers,
and Hieronimo relies on using his own cunning for awhile at
least; here we see that the events will not be the work either of
heaven or of man, but of Revenge sent from the underworld.

CHAPTER 5

Lorenzo's Puppet Shows

FOR the purposes of discussion Act III can be divided into two sections. It contains two units of the plot, the conclusion of Lorenzo's machinations and the start of Hieronimo's counter-action, with the initiative passing from the one to the other in scene vii. There is no chorus or act-break at that point, however, and it seems that Kyd thought of the two actions as being united through the question whether Hieronimo must become a dissembling Machiavel like Lorenzo. Hieronimo and Lorenzo confront each other only at the beginning and at the end of Act III. Throughout the act, the dramatic focus shifts back and forth between them in a complex way that makes us feel the "complication" of the play not simply as a conflict between the two but as an exploration of the complex character of the revenger and his problems. In the action of Hieronimo we reach the play's innermost study of revenge. We have worked our way from Revenge and Andrea through Bel-imperia's revenge against Balthazar and through Lorenzo and Balthazar's revenge against Horatio; and we can now think about the implications of Hieronimo's thoughts and actions against the background of these other revenges.

Act III, Scene i

Scene i, which takes place in the Portuguese court, shows the triumph of justice in the exoneration of Alexandro and in the condemnation of Villuppo. This concluding part of the subplot is a sort of prologue to Act III, marking the act as a unit that will carry us past the crisis of the play to the point where Hieronimo condemns Lorenzo and Balthazar to die.

The ambiguous relation of this scene to the main plot points to the crucial ambiguities of the play as a whole. The Viceroy is wrong to believe that his son has been murdered. Is Hieronimo

right to believe all that he does about Horatio and his murder?
The answer to this question depends on the answers to other
questions. Is Horatio, like Villuppo, a man who uses a false
account of the battle to promote his own selfish interests? Or is
Horatio like Alexandro, an innocent victim, so that only Lorenzo
is like Villuppo in being a Machiavel? In Act III.ii, Hieronimo
finds a letter accusing Lorenzo and Balthazar of the murder of
Horatio. If he believes this letter, will he be like the Viceroy
when he accepts the false tale of Villuppo or when he accepts
the truth of the letter from the Spanish King? If Hieronimo
wrongly accuses Lorenzo and Balthazar, he will be in the position of Villuppo, and will suffer a like fate. Finally, is the Viceroy
primarily a justicer or a revenger—or does the difference between
the two turn out to be slight?

This scene reverses the action of the first scene of the Alexandro-Villuppo subplot (I.iii), but Kyd maintains suspense by
making it start off as if it is to be merely a recapitulation and
extension of the earlier action, and therefore bound to lead to the
death of Alexandro. Once again the scene begins with the
Viceroy pitying himself and blaming Fortune for his plight. As
a ruler he is "plac'd upon extremest height" and is threatened
by the danger of falling (3). To look downward is to be dizzied
and to be forced to close his eyes. Other men can hardly be seen
as forms of himself from such a height. They seem to be looking
up with envy, and their love is therefore to be feared as flattery.
Much better to have their fear, although that too may be flattery
(10–11).

Following this speech, a Nobleman, Villuppo, and the Viceroy
summarize the supposed situation in case we have forgotten the
first scene of the subplot. The retelling is all ironic. The nameless
Nobleman speaks of the surprising wickedness of *Alexandro's*
words and heart, and Villuppo has the nerve to condemn Alexandro for hypocrisy. The truth about whose words are really
wicked is ironically implied when the Viceroy says "No more
Villuppo, thou hast said enough,/And with thy words thou
slay'st our wounded thoughts" (25–26). The irony is so strong
that it impresses upon us the Viceroy's deafness to the reality
behind Villuppo's behavior.

When Alexandro is brought in to be executed, instead of bearing his fate calmly, he is angry, like the Viceroy and Villuppo;

but in other respects he contrasts with these two. The contrast with the Viceroy is particularly important. They are both in extremes: the Viceroy is at a great height of authority, and Alexandro is at a great depth of helpless subjection to authority (31–46). The Viceroy has spoken of himself as a victim of Fortune, but he is too high to see Alexandro as a form of himself and as a real sufferer from the injustices of the "infect" world that Fortune and "wrong" govern (34, 36). The Viceroy has projected his own guilt onto Alexandro and his injustice onto Fortune; Alexandro sees the corruption of the world in realistic terms. The Viceroy's base nature coupled with his high place makes him fear, but Alexandro's noble nature will not let him "stoop" to fear even when he is brought low (40–41).

The Viceroy, still as unjust as he was when Villuppo first made his accusation, once again refuses to listen to Alexandro's denials. He orders Alexandro bound to the stake and burned in fires that prefigure Revenge's treatment of Andrea's enemies at the end of the play. Kyd builds up the suspense of Alexandro's brush with death by making the dialogue go on as long as possible before having the Ambassador enter just as, presumably, an attendant is bending to light the tinder. Villuppo's denunciation of Alexandro at this crucial moment as an "Injurious traitor, monstrous homicide" makes the most of the reversal that occurs when Villuppo is revealed to be the real traitor and would-be homicide (57).

The Viceroy is surprised to learn the truth, but he reacts with characteristic violence: he immediately condemns Villuppo as an "accursed wretch" and barely stops to rejoice that Balthazar is alive (63–75). Although wrath so easily and so tragically sweeps aside thoughts of love, there is no question that the Viceroy is pleased with the new state of affairs. He takes pleasure in restoring Alexandro to his good graces and in commanding the bitterest extremes of torture for Villuppo. It never occurs to him that he must share the responsibility for the injustice to Alexandro, but he is most bitter about the supposed injustice he suffers from those above and below him.

Before Villuppo is dragged off to his death, one point remains to be cleared up. The question is the same as Hieronimo's in the scene before this one, "O wicked butcher, . . . /How could thou strangle virtue and desert?" (II.v.30–31). What could possibly motivate so monstrous a villainy as Villuppo's? Appallingly, it took no very great passion (III.i.90–96), for man's most ignoble drives can make him do as great evils as his most immense passions can, just as Lorenzo thinks. Base greed moves Pedringano, petty ambition moves Villuppo, and envious pride of position moves Lorenzo to the ugliest crimes man can commit.

At the end of this scene, all is well with Alexandro, with Spanish-Portuguese relations, and with the Viceroy. It is easy to forget that all only *appears* to be well with Balthazar. Alexandro did not kill him, but this scene is placed between the scene that provides a direct cause for his death in the murder of Horatio and the scene that provides Hieronimo with his first inkling that Balthazar was one of the murderers.

Act III, Scene ii

Hieronimo is in an extreme position that is different from those of the Viceroy and Alexandro in scene i. He is not at the height of authority where he can indulge his feelings by acting directly and without due caution, nor is he suffering a deep helplessness in which he can look *only* to heaven for relief. As he speaks of the injustice of the world, he does not mention Fortune as a threatening power but rather questions the justice of heaven. Hieronimo does not go so far as to assert that the heavens *are* unjust, but his rhetoric leaves him close to such an assertion. Instead, he says that *if* he gets no revenge for Horatio, *then* that will make it impossible for men to call the heavens just. This logic is of the sort decried by Christian teaching as a blasphemous temptation of God.

The murder of his son destroys Hieronimo's every notion of reality. He suddenly finds himself an isolated stranger in his own world, for nothing is what it appears to be or what it *was* when he was sure of justice. As I have shown in Chapter II, reality has been shattered into a series of elements, "Eyes, life, world, heavens, hell, night, and day," whose relations to one another he can express only in the logic of a parallel series and in their implied action in response to his predicament: "See, search, shew, send, some man, some mean, that may" (III.ii.22–23).

The "Eyes, no eyes" rhetoric of the first part of this speech expresses the disjunction between what Hieronimo thought he knew and what he has tragically found to be true. This rhetoric is no longer needed when he turns to things that his new vision has brought him to experience, the world of dark nights and evil dreams. From the outrage and questioning of the early part of the speech the tone becomes that of a somber despair:

> The night, sad secretary to my moans,
> With direful visions wake my vexed soul,
> And with the wounds of my distressful son
> Solicit me for notice of his death.
> The ugly fiends do sally forth of hell,
> And frame my steps to unfrequented paths,
> And fear my heart with fierce inflamed thoughts.
> The cloudy day my discontents records,
> Early begins to register my dreams
> And drive me forth to seek the murderer.
> Eyes, life, world, heavens, hell, night, and day,
> See, search, shew, send, some man, some mean, that may—
> > *A letter falleth.* (12–23)

Night, hell, and day each has its own structure of alliteration. The four lines on night all alliterate on *w, v, d, m, n,* and *s.* The first and fourth lines define the basic sense of the whole passage. The second and third lines, which expand the thought in terms of a vision, have a heavy, hypnotic rhythm that is felt the more strongly because of the use of alliteration: "*v*isions . . . *v*exed" is the sense of the second line of the four, and this line is linked with the next by the pattern "*w*ith . . . *w*ake . . ./ . . . *w*ith . . . *w*ounds."

In the three lines on hell the hypnotic effect increases as complexity gives way to more obvious parallelism in syntax and to a monotone that can be felt in the insistent repetition of *f.* These lines suggest the awful depths to which Hieronimo has been brought as he comes into the power of Revenge, who is now framing his steps.

The first line on day signals a break with what has gone before in its new pattern of alliteration on *c, r,* and *d.* The words become hard and harsh, the meter more irregular, as Hieronimo returns from his dark reverie to the present light of day and to an immediate and painful awareness of the compulsion that "drives" him forth to seek the murderer. This awareness leads him to the closing couplet in which his mind suddenly sees not only the

whole pattern he has developed but also what he needs from the
world around him. Reality returns to his field of vision, even if
it does not appear in a shape that he can recognize well enough
to deal with in a normal way. When Bel-imperia's letter falls to
him, he is not sure at first that it is a letter; and, when he has
read it, he is not sure he can trust what it says. Yet he does *see*
now, and his language changes from the rhetoric of emotion and
dreams to a plainer style that moves from point to point of the
external world in a clear and logical fashion (24–52).

In the letter Bel-imperia accuses Lorenzo and Balthazar of
the murder of Horatio and urges Hieronimo to take revenge.
From his experience as a judge, Hieronimo has learned to seek
proofs and to find out relationships of cause and effect between
people's characters and their deeds. He has already raised the
question whether any human could be so monstrous as to kill
Horatio (II.v.19–21, 30–31), and in the present passage, therefore, it is not surprising that he can think of no reason for Lorenzo
and Balthazar to hate his son. More important still, he can see
no reason for Bel-imperia to accuse her own brother even if he is
guilty. This telling point certainly justifies his suspicion of the
letter, although second thoughts about the improbability of such
an accusation might make him realize that no forger would in-
vent so weak a story. Hieronimo continues to believe that blood
relations will treat each other as form of themselves and not as
enemies. He does not know that the tragic events of his world
may break such bonds, or that, for example, his wish to kill for
his son is a questionable expression of the bond of love between
father and son: "Dear was the life of my beloved son,/And of his
death behoves me be reveng'd" (III.ii.44–45).

Hieronimo's behavior contrasts completely with that of the
Viceroy when Villuppo made his accusation against Alexandro.
The Viceroy was in a position to achieve his revenge directly,
even if he should blunder along the way, but Hieronimo is not
in such a position and he is by nature and profession more judicious, even in passion. He knows that if he errs he will get no
second chance, and he knows too that he is not of high enough
position to strike his enemies with impunity. Therefore he must
fear, be cautious, and test the accusation before acting on it. It
is worth noting that he is cautious only for his own and Horatio's
sakes: he does not add the thought that caution will prevent him

from being unjust to Lorenzo and Balthazar. His human sympathies are slowly being strangled, and have already become confined to his own flesh and blood, dead and living.

When Hieronimo meets Lorenzo and Pedringano and asks for Bel-imperia, they immediately suspect that he suspects, especially when he refuses to tell them his business and acts oddly in parting from them. His tragic predicament cuts him off from these men as indeed it cuts him off from virtually everyone. He can talk only to himself and to the heavens. His exit line, characteristically addressed to no one, expresses his feeling in a sententious manner: "My grief no heart, my thoughts no tongue can tell" (67). After Hieronimo has gone, Lorenzo and Pedringano compare notes on his suspicious behavior, and Lorenzo, deciding that Serberine has betrayed them, orders Pedringano to kill his fellow servant.

The manipulation of Pedringano is a masterpiece of irony. First, Pedringano gives Serberine a perfect alibi, saying that since the murder Serberine "hath not left my company" (73). This alibi also implies that Pedringano has had as much opportunity to be false as Serberine has had. In the present situation Pedringano and Serberine are pretty much forms of each other, so that if Pedringano kills Serberine, he will be killing himself. All that Lorenzo says to Pedringano about Serberine is actually true of Pedringano himself: "his condition's such,/As fear or flattering words may make him false" (74–75). We do not know whether fear and words can make Serberine false, but we have witnessed their power to conquer Pedringano.

Lorenzo is, in fact, describing Pedringano's "condition" or "humour" (74, 76). The irony becomes unmistakable when Lorenzo says he knows Pedringano is as "secret as my soul" (79). We remember that Bel-imperia thought Pedringano to be as "trusty as my second self," and Lorenzo made him false to her (II.iv.9). "Hearken to me," Lorenzo says: words and rewards are once again to make Pedringano false, this time in the killing of a friend (III.ii.81–93). Pedringano completely misses the irony of Lorenzo's last promise, that he will mount for his deed (92–93). The poor devil should perhaps remember that Lorenzo said much the same thing when they hanged Horatio: "Although his life were still ambitious proud,/Yet is he at the highest now he is dead" (II.iv.60–61). But, if Pedringano cannot see himself in

Serberine, how could he be expected to see himself in Horatio?

Pedringano departs, and Lorenzo commands a Page to tell Serberine where to be, then plans to continue his remote control of the action by giving the Watch orders to stand by at the spot where Serberine and Pedringano are to meet. The scene, which began with Hieronimo's soliloquy on the horror of the world being no world but a mass of public wrongs in which the justice of heaven is thwarted, ends with Lorenzo's soliloquy expounding the kind of policy that makes the world appear as it does to Hieronimo:

> Thus must we work that will avoid distrust,
> Thus must we practice to prevent mishap,
> And thus one ill another must expulse.
> This sly enquiry of Hieronimo
> For Bel-imperia breeds suspicion,
> And this suspicion bodes a further ill.
> As for myself, I know my secret fault,
> And so do they, but I have dealt for them.
> They that for coin their souls endangered,
> To save my life, for coin shall venture theirs:
> And better it's that base companions die,
> Than by their life to hazard our good haps.
> Nor shall they live, for me to fear their faith:
> I'll trust myself, myself shall be my friend,
> For die they shall, slaves are ordain'd to no other end.
> (105–19)

Lorenzo, no less isolated from other men than Hieronimo, does not really communicate with people but uses words to manipulate and mislead them. The key to Lorenzo's isolation is the line "I'll trust myself, myself shall be my friend" (118). His monstrous egotism divorces him from all love of others; as this line implies, he will not even remain true to Balthazar for long, but will use and deceive him too when he has the need (III.iv.27–49).

Lorenzo's mind appears to be working logically as he explains why he acts as he does. It is not a matter of personal will, he insists, but of obvious principles that make it so he "must" work in this way (III.ii.105–6). The principles are associated with the popular notion of Machiavelli, but their application has become entirely selfish rather than politically intended to preserve the state. One principle is that "one ill another must expulse" (107). Ills grow in chains of cause and effect (110), so they must be destroyed in similar chains. But then Lorenzo comes to the real center of his concern: "As for myself" (111). He thinks he is vastly different from his henchmen, who were moved by fear and by hope of worldly promotion, and are base fellows. There is a principle to apply to them: "For die they shall, slaves are ordain'd to no other end" (119).

Lorenzo does not see that he too is motivated by an envious concern for his own worldly position and authority. He does not recognize that fear and not wisdom really governs his murderous scheme: "Nor shall they live, for me to fear their faith" (117). Pedringano and Serberine will not live for him to fear their faith simply because he *now* fears their faith and so kills them. Pedringano and Serberine have no motive to betray themselves and their masters, but Lorenzo is fearfully and foolishly forcing Pedringano into a corner where at last he will have nothing to lose by incriminating him. Lorenzo is not a complete fool; he realizes that this is the weak spot in his plan, and the rest of his scheming is designed to keep Pedringano from talking before he hangs. But we see that each of his clever stratagems creates a new danger that is greater by far than the one it removes.

The movement of this scene from Hieronimo's soliloquy to Lorenzo's indicates the roundabout nature of the combat between them and shows the way the initiative passes back to Lorenzo after appearing briefly to have fallen into Hieronimo's hands. The two men could hardly differ more greatly than they now seem to do. Hieronimo is given reason to suspect Lorenzo, but he moves cautiously to test his suspicion before taking any action. Lorenzo is given reason to suspect Hieronimo, and without any hesitation or investigation he undertakes to kill two other men. Hieronimo knows that his eyes deceive him, that evil forces may be directing his steps to strange paths, and so he achieves a certain wisdom. Lorenzo thinks he is wise and trusts his eyes without question—and the greater fool he.

Act III, Scene iii

In each of the sequences of action leading to murder, there is at least one scene in which some of the characters act as an audience in addition to Revenge and Andrea. This is true of the two love scenes that end in the murder of Horatio, it is true of the murder of Serberine in the present scene, and it will of course be true of the murders in the play-within-the-play. These are the bloody moments in which Revenge's work is most strongly felt, and one important effect of the presence of an audience is to remind us of Revenge as another audience. Thus, as Lorenzo and Balthazar watched the lovers and planned to intervene, we felt the intervention of Revenge and Andrea from above. The present scene, as discussed in Chapter II, depicts the least signifi-cant of the play's murders with the most elaborately developed series of audiences. Revenge and Andrea watch over the Watch, who watch over Pedringano, who watches for Serberine. When Serberine enters, Pedringano steps into action and kills him; and the Watch then steps into action and arrests Pedringano. Off-stage, in the palace, Lorenzo thinks he watches over and acts through them all; but the true manipulator of the action is on the stage in the person of Revenge.

At the beginning of the scene, Pedringano sways back and forth between the desire to advance himself by killing Serberine and the fear that he will ruin himself by the deed:

> Now, Pedringano, bid thy pistol hold,
> And hold on, Fortune! once more favour me,
> Give but success to mine attempting spirit,
> And let me shift for taking of mine aim!
> Here is the gold, this is the gold propos'd:
> It is no dream that I adventure for,
> But Pedringano is possess'd thereof.
> And he that would not strain his conscience
> For him that thus his liberal purse hath stretch'd,
> Unworthy such a favour may he fail,
> And, wishing, want, when such as I prevail.
> As for the fear of apprehension,
> I know, if need should be, my noble lord
> Will stand between me and ensuing harms:
> Besides, this place is free from all suspect.
> Here therefore will I stay and take my stand.
>   (III.iii.1–16)

Like his master, Pedringano has no compunctions about killing; his only question is how he will best be served. His grotesque self-deceptions are typical of the base man who wants to dignify his actions. In a grandiose style he begins with an appeal to Fortune and speaks of his "attempting spirit" as though a sneak murder were an act of manly courage and ambition (1–4). The pretension of this opening is made ludicrous by the fact that his hand is evidently shaking so much that he can scarcely govern the pistol. When thoughts of his "attempting spirit" are not enough to steady him, he tries to reassure himself with the real presence of the solid yellow stuff that is his reward: forget the spirit; he has gold. But then this too worldly and selfish view needs a bit of moralizing to soften it; he must "strain his conscience"—commit murder—as a virtuous deed to show himself worthy of his master's liberality. Such an excellent perversion of evil into good is what we should expect of a man who has sold his soul, his "attempting spirit," to a devil like Lorenzo. But the man who inverts reality, sinking to low deeds in order to rise, inevitably "mounts" only to fall in the halter when things "alter."

When the Watch and Serberine enter, they tell us that they have been ordered to this spot by powers above them in the world's hierarchy. Pedringano screws up his courage and shoots:

PED. Here comes the bird that I must seize upon:
     Now, Pedringano, or never play the man!
SER. I wonder that his lordship stays so long,
     Or wherefore should he send for me so late?
PED. For this, Serberine, and thou shalt ha't.
                 Shoots the dag [a pistol].
     So, there he lies, my promise is perform'd. (28–33)

Pedringano reduces his victim to a bird and flatters himself that he "plays the man"—no doubt with an "attempting spirit"—in committing a cowardly murder. Serberine's question is one that Pedringano should ponder, but he can see no farther than the end of his friend's life and his reward, both of which are in plain view.

Pedringano squeezes the trigger and the man dies, but Pedringano has not killed him or even strained his conscience; he has merely performed his promise to Lorenzo and is no doubt worthy of his master's liberality. The outcries of the Watch remind us of what has actually happened:

1. Hark gentlemen, this is a pistol shot.
2. And here's one slain; stay the murderer. (34–35)

Pedringano has still got reality standing on its head, however. Without the least self-awareness he can swear "by the sorrows of the souls in hell" that he will play the *priest* by *killing* those who seize him (36–37). The Watch continue to try to bring Pedringano to reality, saying he should play the priest by confessing instead of killing, and describing his deed as unkind—as unnatural. Secure in his topsy-turvy view of things, Pedringano is impudent to the last. He is shaken momentarily by the news that they will take him to Hieronimo, of all people, but he knows that above Hieronimo stands Lorenzo, the real power in his life and his protector. He strikes a pose and cries "do your worst, for I defy you all" (48). Lorenzo would enjoy the irony of that line, and so should Revenge.

Act III, Scene iv

Balthazar is hapless and confused where his love for Belimperia is involved, and up to now Lorenzo has seemed clearheaded by comparison. In the present scene, however, in their discussion of the danger that they have been betrayed, Balthazar seems quite reasonable as compared with the confused Lorenzo, who *thinks* he is clearheaded and keeps congratulating himself on his cunning. One speech of Lorenzo's here clarifies his conduct:

> A guilty conscience, urged with the thought
> Of former evils, easily cannot err:
> I am persuaded, and dissuade me not,
> That all's revealed to Hieronimo. (III.iv.14–17)

Lorenzo's conscience may not be strong enough to make him suffer anguish, but guilt will take some kind of hurtful effect on any man, even one as pitiless as Lorenzo. He does have pity for himself, so his sense of guilt makes him fearful for his own safety.

Lorenzo is perhaps about to tell Balthazar how he has undertaken to destroy Serberine and Pedringano when the Page enters with the news of Serberine's murder and of Pedringano's arrest (20–37). Although Balthazar will kill an enemy, he has normal human sympathies for those who are near him. Serberine loved him, so Balthazar is genuinely moved by his slaying and finds it hard to understand how Pedringano could kill his friend. Lorenzo picks this very moment to betray his friend Balthazar by pretend-

ing to share his innocence and his anger. He wishes to use Balthazar's anger, and does not hesitate to sacrifice sincerity in friendship to ingenious manipulation. In Lorenzo's urging of Balthazar
to complain to the King for revenge there is an ironic foreshadowing of Hieronimo's later complaints, which are blocked by Lorenzo. The irony redounds against Lorenzo, for the consequence
of Balthazar's successful complaints is the death of Pedringano,
and this event leads Hieronimo to go to the King.

Lorenzo is certain that he has been "wise":

> Why so, this fits our former policy,
> And thus experience bids the wise to deal.
> I lay the plot, he prosecutes the point,
> I set the trap, he breaks the worthless twigs
> And sees not that wherewith the bird was lim'd.
> Thus hopeful men, that mean to hold their own,
> Must look like fowlers to their dearest friends.
> He runs to kill whom I have holp to catch,
> And no man knows it was my reaching fatch.
> 'Tis hard to trust unto a multitude,
> Or anyone, in mine opinion,
> When men themselves their secrets will reveal. (38–49)

Lorenzo's "wisdom," which acts from policies he thinks are based
on experience, completely isolates him from other men by making
him manipulate even his "dearest friend." Calculating evil has
made use of human passion in a manner that looks back to the
pattern of the morality plays and looks forward to the pattern of
such a play as *Othello* and Iago's control of the passions of
Roderigo, Cassio, and especially Othello himself. In *The Spanish
Tragedy*, however, the most significant interaction of calculating
evil and tragic passion is internal; it takes place gradually and
desperately in the breast of Hieronimo.

Lorenzo's concern to "hold his own" is an open indication of
the envious drive to maintain his position and power that moti-
vates all his actions (43). The last line of this speech suggests the
futility of his isolating himself from all others behind a wall of
mistrust. If "men themselves their secrets will reveal," then there
can be no safety from betrayal because the individual will always
manage to betray his lonely self, and the rest of the scene shows
how this can happen. When a messenger comes with a letter from

Pedringano, who appeals to Lorenzo for help, Lorenzo sends the
messenger back with assurances that salvation is on its way; then
he sends his Page to Pedringano with money and with a box that
the Page is to say contains a signed pardon: "But open't not, and
if thou lov'st thy life" (73). Lorenzo does not take the Page into
his confidence, and his words literally direct the boy away from
a deed that will betray his scheme. In the next scene, however,
we see that Lorenzo's very effort to make sure the Page does not
look in the box tempts the Page to do so. Thus Lorenzo's own
words betray him to at least one other person. The Page is loyal
to his master, however, and he does not tell Pedringano that the
box is empty, showing how needless it is for Lorenzo to have so
extreme a mistrust of all the servants.

When the Page has raced off to take the box to Pedringano,
Lorenzo is left alone to worry again about the danger of betrayal:

> Now stands our fortune on a tickle point,
> And now or never ends Lorenzo's doubts.
> One only thing is uneffected yet,
> And that's to see the executioner.
> But to what end? I list not trust the air
> With utterance of our pretence therein,
> For fear the privy whisp'ring of the wind
> Convey our words amongst unfriendly ears,
> That lie too open to advantages.
> *E quel che voglio io, nessun lo sa,*
> *Intendo io: quel mi bastera.* (78–88)

Lorenzo's confusion reaches its peak, and he is indeed on a "tickle
point" of doubts. He thinks of making sure of the executioner, but
then cannot be certain that this will not create more danger than
it eliminates (irony piles on irony: the executioner carries Pedringano's incriminating letter to Hieronimo). Lorenzo has trusted
no other man; now he will not even trust the air or his own whispers and is isolating himself more than ever within silence and
paranoia. His last two lines are especially important, for he will
not even trust his own language to say "And what I want, no-one
knows; I understand, and that's enough for me" (Edwards' translation). The first part of this might well stand by itself: *no* one
knows what Lorenzo really wants, not even Lorenzo. "But to
what end?" he has just asked himself. The man who trusts no

one and deceives everyone has come at last to the point where he does not trust himself and where we, at least, can see that he also deceives himself.

Act III, Scene v

In scene v, the Page has probably waited only long enough to be out of Lorenzo's presence before opening the box. As Belimperia disobeyed her father and took Andrea for a lover, so this boy is a typical perverse human. Just as he says, women and boys are alike in this: "that they are most forbidden, they will soonest attempt" (III.v.4–5). The empty box is a fine symbol of the empty promises of princes that men believe in so much that they jest themselves to death.

Act III, Scene vi

In scene vi, Hieronimo is so distraught about the injustice he suffers that he is unable to think about the trial of Pedringano and therefore fails to search for the meaning of Serberine's death. Like the Viceroy earlier, he complains that "neither gods nor men" are just to him, and lets his passion blind him to what is happening (III.vi.10). He cries out for the "justice of the heavens" to help him "know the cause" that will allay his suffering, but he is too impatient to find out the cause of Pedringano's crime (6–7, 15–16).

Pedringano is Impudence itself. The Page has just arrived with promises and the box from Lorenzo, and Pedringano is as impatient as Hieronimo to bring things to an end (23). He mentions another letter he has written Lorenzo reminding him of the murder they performed together; and this letter the Hangman brings to Hieronimo in the next scene. Hieronimo denounces Pedringano for the death of Serberine, just as he would if he knew that he had helped kill Horatio; but it is ironic that he should condemn one of his son's murderers in such appropriate terms while the emotion of the condemnation is itself preventing him from discovering how right he is!

Pedringano jests himself to death, exactly as the Page foresaw that he would. His real hangman, Lorenzo, could talk circles around Pedringano because he hypnotized him with the sight of gold. Pedringano, still hearkening to his master's voice, imagines Lorenzo to have shut his voice up in the box to give his henchman

license to speak in his stead, and we see that he is able to play
with words almost as wittily as his master. He becomes a little
Lorenzo, thinking himself to be the one who controls the action,
and struggling to advance his will by the clever use of words.
Lorenzo claims that cunning can govern the world; Pedringano's
base wit acts out a grotesque parody of this absurd pretension.
The Hangman is taken aback by Pedringano's jesting, for few of
his customers have been so jolly. Yet he manages to counter and
usually top Pedringano's jests. He is even more certain of the
security of his position than Pedringano is, a certainty that will
be shattered in its turn when he finds Pedringano's letter to Lorenzo and fears that he may be made to suffer the fate of his
victim (III.vii.19–28). The contrast between them in the tone of
their jests is skillfully maintained. Pedringano, impudently showing off, makes elaborate, silly jokes; the Hangman, amazed,
angered, and impatient, answers with curt and grim jests (41–
88).

Pedringano will not pray. Unconscious that he is at the "extreme" moment of death, he continues to jest to the very end. His
bizarre conduct in extremity may be contrasted with the shock
of Horatio, the courage of Alexandro, the suicidal despair of
Isabella, and the immense passion of Hieronimo. To the last
Pedringano is the completely foolish Mr. Worldly-Wiseman who
is secure in his faith in a box or in a cunning plot, and is sure that
what is "good for the body is likewise good for the soul" (76–77).

Hieronimo leaves the scene before Pedringano is hanged, saying that "This makes me to remember thee, my son" (98). Although Hieronimo means simply that the spectacle of a hanging
will remind him of his son's death, Pedringano's ambitious desire
to "mount" may also remind us of Horatio, as I argued in Chapter
II. Pedringano epitomizes at a level of obvious foolishness the
general folly of mankind that Hieronimo has just defined before
he is reminded of his son:

> I have not seen a wretch so impudent!
> O monstrous times, where murder's set so light,
> And where the soul, that should be shrin'd in heaven,
> Solely delights in interdicted things,
> Still wand'ring in the thorny passages
> That intercepts itself of happiness. (89–94)

The language of Hieronimo's speech is general enough to apply not only to Pedringano and to the murderers of Horatio, but to the perversity of the Page and Bel-imperia, and even to Hieronimo himself, for "wand'ring in the thorny passages" harks back to "The ugly fiends do sally forth of hell,/And frame my steps to unfrequented paths" (III.ii.16–17).

In his speech that opened this scene, Hieronimo said that neither gods nor men have been just to him. In this last speech before he leaves the stage, he judges the times by the standards of a heavenly justice and of a God who forbids and interdicts foul deeds. As a judge, he wants to think of himself as the agent of such a God, but in his personal quest for justice he has begun to doubt that God cares. Thus far he has consistently maintained that justice is heavenly and that, if justice fails and he turns to revenge, he will be driven by ugly fiends who come from hell (III.ii.5–21; III.vi.1–10, 90–98). The next scene starts with a speech by Hieronimo in which he despairs of heaven's justice, but this time the action of the scene revives his faith almost completely.

Act III, Scene vii

With the hanging of Pedringano the initiative passes from Lorenzo to Hieronimo. There was no letter from Lorenzo for Pedringano in the box, but there was a letter from Pedringano for Lorenzo on the corpse.[1] Lorenzo has silenced himself in his fear that others will hear what he says; Hieronimo cries aloud, but try as he will to be heard, God does not seem to heed him. The contrast of the two is expressed in parallel imagery of words and wind:

> [LOR.] . . . . I list not trust the air
>   With utterance of our pretence therein,
>   For fear the privy whisp'ring of the wind
>   Convey our words amongst unfriendly ears.
> (III.iv.82–85)
>
> HIER. Where shall I run to breathe abroad my woes,
>   My woes, whose weight hath wearied the earth?
>   Or mine exclaims, that have surcharg'd the air
>   With ceaseless plaints for my deceased son?
>   The blust'ring winds, conspiring with my words,
>   At my lament have mov'd the leaveless trees,

> Disrob'd the meadows of their flower'd green,
> Made mountains marsh with spring-tides of my tears,
> And broken through the brazen gates of hell.
> Yet still tormented is my tortur'd soul
> With broken sighs and restless passions,
> That winged mount, and, hovering in the air,
> Beat at the windows of the brightest heavens,
> Soliciting for justice and revenge:
> But they are plac'd in those empyreal heights
> Where, countermur'd with walls of diamond,
> I find the place impregnable, and they
> Resist my woes, and give my words no way.
>
> (III.vii.1–18)

To this moment, Lorenzo, but not Hieronimo, has spoken criminal words that might ruin him if they were heard and understood by others. Up to now, when Hieronimo's action really begins, the old Marshal has wanted to conceal his words only to hide his suspicions of the criminality of others. Not wanting other men to hear his lamentations, he must break away from company, as he has just burst from the execution of Pedringano, before he can release his pent-up feelings. A man driven to run abroad by passion, wherever he goes to weep, it seems to his "eyes, no eyes" that his grief changes the face of nature. He knows from the fiends that have driven him into these unfrequented paths that his words have "broken through the brazen gates of hell."

These effects on the world of nature and on hell are Hieronimo's projection of the destructive effects of grief on his own inner being. Not even these great storms of tears can assuage his grief, however, for the only thing that will satisfy him is for God to show that He has been moved. As Hieronimo feels himself abandoned by God, his thoughts become more stormy and hellish; he is becoming bitter against God, saying that heaven cannot hear him because of its very loftiness and beauty. He thinks heaven is too much isolated from man, too far above us to see us as fellow beings, too impregnable in holy strength to hear our woes. Human pity is blocked by one person's feeling that he is superior to another, and perhaps we project this human failure onto the cosmic order when we conceive of a ruling, judging God who condescendingly grants grace to us in accord with His own will and not in accord with our merit or our despairing cries.

The Hangman enters with Pedringano's letter to Lorenzo. Like Pedringano before him, the executioner wants his master to save him from the gallows. The Hangman has dangled a puppet on a string not knowing that the puppet had already dangled another man on a string, and having no idea that a higher puppeteer might have him swinging. Now he has discovered a frightening image of his own potential fate in Pedringano's corpse, but he could see no likeness while the man lived.

Pedringano's letter, written *in extremis*, contains some of the simplest words of truth in the entire play. When it confirms the earlier letter, showing it indeed to have come from Bel-imperia, Hieronimo's faith in heaven and justice is restored. The despair of "O eyes, no eyes" is resolved in his new "feeling" perception. The dark implication of the earlier "O sacred heavens" that there were none is answered hopefully in the repetition of the phrase followed by a further echo of the earlier speech:

> O sacred heavens, may it come to pass
> That such a monstrous and detested deed,
> So closely smother'd, and so long conceal'd,
> Shall thus by this be venged or reveal'd? (45–48, cf. III.ii.5, 9)
>
> . . . .
> Now may I make compare, 'twixt hers and this,
> Of every accident; I ne'er could find
> Till now, and now I feelingly perceive,
> They did what heaven unpunish'd would not leave. (53–56)

Hieronimo now knows who his enemies are and where he should run to breathe abroad his woes. The thing for which he curses Lorenzo is his falseness, his "flattering looks" that concealed murderous intent (57). In stressing the great evil of false friendship, Hieronimo establishes a standard by which we may later judge his own actions. Lorenzo is a false friend, but Balthazar has been an enemy from start to finish; and Hieronimo curses everything about the man, including, significantly, "the cause of these constrained wars" (61). The broad conflict between Spain and Portugal is brought within the scope of Hieronimo's wrath and so, later on, of his revenge.

At the beginning of the scene Hieronimo grieved that his words of lamentation could not penetrate heaven, but at the end of the scene he believes that heaven has heard him. He need grieve no more in lonely despair; lamentation has become a "waste" of "unfruitful words" (67). He means to end his isolation and to cry aloud to the King for blood, the only thing that can satisfy him (68). If words demanding justice are ignored, he will turn his tongue to threats of revenge (73).

CHAPTER 6

Hieronimo Beware: Go by, Go by

Act III, Scene viii

THE lamentations of Isabella in scene viii remind us of Hieronimo's outburst at the start of scene vii; but, where he was saved from lunacy by finding relief in a way to pursue revenge, Isabella, who can only expend her grief against herself, goes mad. Her Maid has offered herbs to purge her eye and head, but Isabella does not feel a loss of vision and understanding as Hieronimo does. She suffers an agony of heartbreak from a sense of an irremediable loss: no medicine can cure her because none can bring the dead back to life. Isabella wants revenge, like Hieronimo, but she has not allowed hate of the murderers to come near to supplanting love of the lost one: "Horatio! O where's Horatio?" (III.viii.6).

Isabella's Maid tries to comfort her by saying Horatio is in the Elysian fields, and when Isabella replies in words of madness, the Maid says her mistress's agony torments her soul. Isabella scoffs at the idea that her servant, to her a mere puppet, might have a soul for suffering; and she rejects the Maid's placement of Horatio's soul in the pagan underworld, speaking in a way that echoes Hieronimo's speech at the start of the preceding scene (cf. III.vii.10–14 and III.viii.13–22). The great difference between the two speeches is that Hieronimo's soul seeks justice and revenge, whereas in her madness Isabella has found Horatio in heaven. And then her vision of innocence and harmony yields to a darkness in which she rushes off to find the murderers. Again she echoes Hieronimo: "Wither shall I run?" (III.viii.24; cf. III.-vii.1). Her running is, however, purposeless, a surrender to despair and insanity. Although Hieronimo's mind is held together by a purpose that at least seems rational, he is perhaps less sane than Isabella in the final analysis.

Act III, Scene ix

Bel-imperia "sequester'd from the court" is a dramatic image of human isolation (III.ix.2). She has been shut away by Lorenzo partly because of her own egotism and passion, and partly because of Lorenzo's egotism and Balthazar's passion. She knows even less about her predicament than does Hieronimo about his. Her blindness is symbolized by her wish that Andrea could see how she suffers, for he is in plain sight on stage, as always.

This is the third consecutive scene of lamentation. First Hieronimo cried out and was given a course to pursue; then Isabella grieved and rushed out on a mad quest that mocked the final emptiness of Hieronimo's course; and now Bel-imperia laments, but she has not even the freedom to run away. She has no choice but to accept her helpless state and to make the best of it in pious terms (12–14). In her extreme state here just before her release from imprisonment, it is perhaps important that in speaking of a need for patience, she echoes the dialogue of the parallel subplot shortly before Alexandro was released from bondage (III.i.31–35).

Act III, Scene x

Scene x follows almost immediately after the hanging of Pedringano, for the Page has just completed his report to Lorenzo when the scene begins. We are given the idea of two fast-moving lines of action: while Hieronimo has received news of the hanging, the Page has been on his way to Lorenzo. Now, while the Page reports to Lorenzo, Hieronimo is hurrying to court to make his accusations before the King. The events of scene x send Lorenzo to court, too, and there he and Hieronimo at last clash directly.

With the death of Pedringano certain, Lorenzo feels relief (III.x.3–5). At the very moment when he has been betrayed as he feared he would be, Lorenzo is entirely confident that he is secure. The falseness of his security is implied by the reference to "him with whom he [Pedringano] sojourns now" (5). Lorenzo presumably intends the devil in hell, but a bit of Pedringano dwells with Hieronimo, and is not some element of Pedringano going to remain with Revenge?

The death of Pedringano has supposedly made it safe to release Bel-imperia. In some ways this scene is the reverse of Act

II.i, where the action looked forward to the murder of Horatio, and where the talk between Lorenzo and Balthazar moved from Balthazar's love of Bel-imperia to his hatred of Horatio. Now, as the action looks back on the murder of Horatio, the dialogue moves from the talk of murder to love and courtship. We are not to forget that Balthazar proceeds to the marriage he hopes for with blood on his hands.

Lorenzo's advice to the lovelorn is grotesque (17–23), for he has no conception of love as passion or as a human relationship of mutual concern and trust. His lack of human feeling may be heard in the phrase "As for her sweetheart"—some real attention is necessary to catch this as a reference to Horatio's murder— "Jest with her gently" (21–22). Feigned jests may indeed conceal deadly realities. Pedringano jested his way to the gallows, and now Lorenzo and Balthazar, equally confident in a false sense of security, follow in his footsteps.

As Bel-imperia enters, Lorenzo greets her as "sister," but she angrily replies that his cruel actions have denied that relationship (24–34). In response to her questions as to why he killed Horatio and locked her up, Lorenzo relates another false story. By now the man is almost totally incapable of communicating truthfully with anyone, and he is slowly but surely becoming the prisoner of the world of lies he has been creating. Lorenzo's lies succeeded with Pedringano, and since he does not understand that his sister is different, he cannot perceive her true reaction to his lies. He finds his story plausible; therefore he accepts at face value the "peace" she eventually makes with him. In the final mutual pretense of the play-within-the-play, however, he comes upon the truth. Although Lorenzo's story is false in fact, it is true to his character and his values. He lies when he says he murdered Horatio and locked Bel-imperia up because the King was coming and there would have been trouble if Bel-imperia had been found with a socially inferior lover. Nevertheless, it is true that an egotistical sense of family honor and of Horatio's social inferiority had a great deal to do with Lorenzo's personal motivation for the murder.

Bel-imperia, who scorns the whole performance, sums up Lorenzo's story and Balthazar's eager support of it with obvious sarcasm (62–67). In the end, she lets Lorenzo think that she believes his explanations; and he therefore adopts a new tone of voice and turns from the violence of the past to the "love" of the present (71–82). The eloquence of Lorenzo's new voice is not lost on Bel-imperia, and she takes the occasion to comment ironically on his mastery of "politic" words (83–86). The "experience" that has made him an "orator," which she says is not known to her, is perhaps his success with Pedringano and Balthazar. And Bel-imperia's contempt for Balthazar's artificial love-talk is no less than her contempt for her brother's politic or eloquent words (87–95). No one of the three is talking in an honest, natural way. Each is isolated behind a mask of verbal control; and Lorenzo's false words, Bel-imperia's ironic praises, and Balthazar's hapless artifices are evidence of the same human malaise.

Lorenzo has spoken of Bel-imperia's hate and Balthazar's love meeting in the present moment (82)—an oversimplification of the emotional situation. As Bel-imperia detects, the romantic talk of Balthazar implies that he suffers "love, and fear, and both at once" (93). She pretends that the inferior wit of a woman cannot manage so important a combination, but she then shows her witty mastery of both men by defining such a combination in a way that puts Balthazar's love and Lorenzo's friendship in a very poor light: "They joined dismayed dread to quaking fear, a futile deed of sottish betrayal" (Edwards' translation of Kyd's Latin in lines 102–3). She has pointed her finger directly at the principle that really governs Lorenzo's wisdom: an egotistical fear that inevitably betrays. Lorenzo's wisdom is entirely negative in cause as well as in effect. He tries to make up for his lack of feelings by adopting a pose of knowing best; for example, we witness his advice to the lovelorn at lines 17–23. Here, as elsewhere, he attaches himself to the passions of others and asserts his ego by seeking dominance over them. At the center of all is a quaking fear of the void that is at the heart of his being.

In the last lines of this scene Balthazar takes his place in the "whither shall I run" pattern of hopelessness that helps to define the unity of action in this part of the play:

> Led by the loadstar of her heavenly looks,
> Wends poor oppressed Balthazar,
> As o'er the mountains walks the wanderer,
> Incertain to effect his pilgrimage.
> (106–9; cf. III.vii.1, 69;
> III.viii.24; III.xi.11ff; III.xii.6ff)

Act III, Scene xi

The motif of the hopeless quest is the chief subject of scene xi.
When two Portuguese ask Hieronimo the way to the Duke's
house, he points to where it stands, but when they ask if Lorenzo
is to be found there, his mind begins to crack and he gives a
different set of directions (III.xi.10–29). This passage echoes
Andrea's description of the left-hand path to the deepest hell
(I.i.63–71), and shows that Hieronimo has understood the working of Lorenzo's mind as well as Bel-imperia has. A guilty deed
has led Lorenzo to distrust and fear; he has not yet followed the
path on to despair, but Hieronimo knows the way because he is
talking from his own experience of distrust and fear. The melancholy and the suicidal despair are Hieronimo's reaction to "the
world's iniquities" (III.xi.22). Lorenzo passes from a guilty deed
to fearful distrust and on to death and hell. Does not Hieronimo
go something like a reverse journey from his son's hell-born death
to his own melancholy and despair, to fearful distrust of others,
and finally to dreadful deeds?

Act III, Scene xii

In scene xii and the next the crisis of the play occurs. Hieronimo, who stands poised between suicide, justice, and revenge,
rejects the first, tries to obtain the second, and is driven finally
to seek revenge when the King cannot understand him. As we
shall see, Hieronimo's search for justice is frustrated in part by his
despair of justice, his longing for revenge and then death. Even
before he tries to approach the King, he has convinced himself
that he will fail, and is ready and anxious to kill himself and go
to the fiery judge in the underworld (III.xii.1–19). What keeps
him alive is that he is personally vindictive in his quest for justice:
if he kills himself, he believes he can obtain a fair judgment
against Horatio's murderers in the underworld; but then he would
not be alive to kill Lorenzo and Balthazar (13–18). Only the
punishment of those two by his own means can satisfy his soul.

Hieronimo's mind is again devoted to obsessive imaginings of
hell, as it was in scene xi. The rich imagery and hypnotic rhythm
of his language reveal that the dark underworld increasingly possesses his soul. His obsession made him unable to give a rational
answer to the two Portuguese men in scene xi, and in this scene

he is again isolated from others, able to speak in soliloquy, but, as he fears he will be, stricken "mute" when the King and his court enter (4–5,25–31). Hieronimo's "beware: go by, go by" shows that he has reached the "forest of distrust and fear" that he spoke of in scene xi, and sure enough he finds Lorenzo equally involved in that "darksome place and dangerous to pass" (III.xi.-15–16, III.xii.31).

The King is just as deeply engrossed as Hieronimo is in his own concerns. The concerns of a ruler are broader than those of the individual, yet they can make him deaf to others. While Hieronimo goes by and lurks morosely at the edge of the stage, the King and the Portuguese Ambassador talk happily of a father and son whose fate so far contrasts point by painful point with Hieronimo and Horatio's. The Ambassador says the Viceroy is "a man extremely overjoy'd/To hear his son so princely entertain'd,/Whose death he had so solemnly bewail'd" (III.xii.34–36). The news of Balthazar's impending marriage to Bel-imperia is "more delightful to his soul,/Than myrrh or incense to the offended heavens" (41–42). There is a double irony in comparing the Viceroy's spirit with that of heaven, and in referring to the "offended heavens" without any realization that the heavens may be offended by the news of the impending marriage.

The Ambassador goes on to report that the Viceroy is so pleased that he is coming to the wedding himself. To show his great desire for a lasting peace, he has decided to abdicate his throne and to make Balthazar and Bel-imperia the rulers of Portugal. Since the King of Spain has already promised his kingdom to their male issue, the wedding is to make two kingdoms into one as it is to unite two young people into one flesh. Two individuals are supposed to find themselves in each other when they wed, thereby ending their isolation. But in the case of Bel-imperia and Balthazar there can be no hope of such a union since the past has wrought too deep a division between them, as perhaps it also has between Spain and Portugal.

Hieronimo is sensitive to any suggestion that his caution in revenge indicates a slackness in his devotion to Horatio. Therefore when the Duke speaks of the Viceroy's "wondrous zeal to Balthazar his son," Hieronimo may again be hurt by the implicit contrast (54). The royal talk now turns to the relation between Balthazar and Horatio, making the contrast explicit (57–78). The connection between *ransom* for Balthazar and his *return* affects Hieronimo, for nothing can make Horatio able to return from death. Horatio was a treasure in himself, and the loss of such a son bankrupts Hieronimo in a way that leaves all the gold in Portugal worthless. Hieronimo cries aloud for justice, but the thought that payment cannot redeem his loss breaks his mind and returns it to its new home in the underworld, where he will find hellish fiends to get revenge. Once more his emotional need carries him beyond the point where he can be satisfied by a judgment that agrees upon ransoms and repayments. He can never be satisfied unless he somehow inflicts upon his enemies the same hell that they have inflicted upon him. And this demand the King does not understand at all, for he is not told that Horatio has been murdered by Lorenzo and Balthazar.

The King does not understand Hieronimo's pleas because, as we have noted, he is engrossed in his own affairs and also because Hieronimo abandons hope of being heard and begins to talk madly instead of telling the King what has happened. It is important to note that the King does not realize that he denies justice to Hieronimo; indeed, he very patiently bears with the old man in his madness, despite Lorenzo's efforts to discredit him. Lorenzo characteristically accuses Hieronimo of the "extreme pride" and envious covetousness that are his own motivation by saying that Hieronimo is a lunatic with lofty notions of his son's worth (85–89). The King, however, who does not even know that Horatio is dead, generously interprets Hieronimo's zeal for his son as no more than the normal "love that fathers bear their sons" (91). The payment, which now means nothing to Hieronimo, the King very justly wants him to have as "his due" (93).

Lorenzo continues to try to use Hieronimo's madness to injure him, suggesting that he should lose his position as Marshal; but the King echoes Hieronimo's own initial caution in pursuit of justice: " 'Tis best that we see further in it first" (100). The scene ends with talk of sealing the match between Bel-imperia and Balthazar by a formal betrothal. As usual when Kyd leaves a group of characters for a time, he gives us some notion of what they will be doing while we are watching some other scene of action.

Act III, Scene xiii

The soliloquy of Hieronimo that opens scene xiii is the crisis-within-the-crisis of the play. Human justice has seemed to fail, and Hieronimo has stumbled from the court, conscious of being driven by devils. This soliloquy is his last pause before he plunges down the left-hand pathway into darkness. If the orderly procedures of human justice have failed, can Hieronimo count on heavenly justice to intervene in some fashion, or must he take affairs into his own hands and seek revenge? If he enacts a bloody revenge, can he justify it to himself or to heaven? Since this soliloquy is the most difficult as well as the most crucial passage in the play,[1] we must analyze it in detail. In the first half of the speech Hieronimo finally decides to seek revenge, and in the second half he decides on the means he will use. In his debate on revenge, his lines read:

> *Vindicta Mihi!*
> Ay, heaven will be reveng'd of every ill,
> Nor will they suffer murder unrepaid:
> Then stay, Hieronimo, attend their will,
> For mortal men may not appoint their time.
> *Per scelus semper tutum est sceleribus iter.*
> Strike, and strike home, where wrong is offer'd thee,
> For evils unto ills conductors be,
> And death's the worst of resolution:
> For he that thinks with patience to contend
> To quiet life, his life shall easily end.
> *Fata si miseros juvant, habes salutem;*
> *Fata si vitam negant, habes sepulchrum.*
> If destiny thy miseries do ease,
> Then hast thou health, and happy shalt thou be:
> If destiny deny thee life, Hieronimo,
> Yet shalt thou be assured of a tomb:
> If neither, yet let this thy comfort be,
> Heaven covereth him that hath no burial.
> And to conclude, I will revenge his death! (III.xiii.1–20)

"*Vindicta Mihi*" is the biblical "Vengeance is mine, I will repay, saith the Lord," an injunction against private revenge. In the next two lines Hieronimo expresses faith in heavenly justice. This may seem a little strange, since we have just heard him speak of himself as one whom the devils drive, but the point is probably that Hieronimo is trying very hard to be reasonable about his predicament. Book in hand, he is trying to work his way from first principles to determine a course of action, and he may have already succeeded in returning himself to the faith he felt when Pedringano's incriminating letter convinced him of heaven's interest in justice (III.vii.45–56).

But between that moment and this one, the King's justice has failed to satisfy him; and so now Hieronimo must again ask himself how the inevitable justice of heaven is to come about. This soliloquy is the "To be or not to be" of *The Spanish Tragedy*. "Then stay, Hieronimo, attend their [heavens] will,/For mortal men may not appoint their time" reveals his contemplation of at least two and maybe three courses: revenge, passive inaction, and possibly suicide. 1) Heaven will appoint the time for revenge, and therefore he must not rashly act to revenge his son, although heaven may use him as an agent. 2) Heaven will revenge, and therefore he need only wait for God to act. 3) Since heaven will revenge, he must stay alive and not appoint the time of his own death in suicide. One of the chief ambiguities here is in "men may not appoint their time." The words seem to say that men may not choose the time of their own action almost as much as they say that men may not choose the time in which the heavens will enact revenge. The idea of suicide as appointing one's own time is also possible.

By line 5, then, although Hieronimo may have contemplated both suicide and immediate action, he seems to have decided to wait for heaven to appoint the time in which to act. But from his first authority, the Bible, he now turns to a second one, a tragedy of Seneca, speaking an adaptation of line 115 of *Agamemnon*: "*per scelera semper sceleribus tutum est iter*"—"The safe way for crime is always through crime" (in Edwards' translation). This line is spoken by Clytemnestra to justify killing Agamemnon, whom she has already wronged, before he can retaliate for the wrong. Hieronimo, who translates this two lines later in "For evils unto ills conductors be," reasons that since his enemies, like Clytemnestra, will follow their murder of Horatio with more crimes, it behooves him to "strike, and strike home." If he does not strike back "where wrong is offer'd" him, he will find that "he that thinks with patience to contend/To quiet life, his life shall easily end." If he stands around with Christian-Stoic "patience," waiting for heaven to appoint the time, his foes will kill him; and, since "death's the worst of" acting resolutely, he has nothing to lose by attempting action. In any case, the worst that will happen is that he will die. Quoting from Seneca's *Troades,* he says that, if he acts, he will either destroy his enemies or they will destroy him (12–16). If he dies, he will have a tomb; or, if he does not have one, heaven itself will be a lofty cover for his body.

"And to conclude, I will revenge his death!" (20). This line ends the first part of the speech, and Hieronimo now turns to the question of the means of revenge. But how has he reached the conclusion that he should revenge Horatio's death? The Christian injunction against private revenge still stands at the head of the speech, and, although he might have done so, Hieronimo has offered no argument to show that, as a *judge,* he might have the authority to assume heaven's authority for himself under the circumstances. Perhaps he sneers when he talks of heaven's revenge, or perhaps he turns with bitterness from a nominal acceptance of the Christian position to an emotionally more satisfying decision to revenge.

There can be no reconciling the two positions within the terms of Hieronimo's speech. He sets up two alternatives and then says "And to conclude, I will revenge his death." *I will,* not heaven will, with no statement to the effect that "I will" be an agent of heaven. And the means that he proceeds to spell out are quite clearly devilish (21–44). There is no use trying to minimize the evil of cloaking revenge under a pretense of friendship (24), for Hieronimo echoes Lorenzo's talk of *his* "revenges" in this part of his speech. He speaks of his *wisdom* in using false pretenses of friendship, as Lorenzo did, forgetting that he has earlier condemned Lorenzo for his perjuries: "O false Lorenzo, are these thy flattering looks?" (III.vii.57). Hieronimo will rely on his own wisdom to pick the right time to act (25–26). In its context this decision is a plain contradiction and rejection of his earlier statement of the Christian principle that "men may not appoint their time" (5).

The vengeful all follow the same course of action because they are solicited by Revenge:

[HIER.]   Thus therefore will I rest me in unrest,
           Dissembling quiet in unquietness. (III.xiii.29–30)

VICE.   Then rest we here awhile in our unrest,
              And feed our sorrows with some inward sighs.
                            (I.iii.5–6)
REVENGE. Content thyself, Andrea; though I sleep,
              Yet is my mood soliciting their souls:
              Sufficeth thee that poor Hieronimo
              Cannot forget his son Horatio.
              Nor dies Revenge although he sleep awhile,
              For in unquiet, quietness is feign'd,
              And slumb'ring is a common worldly wile.
                         (III.xv.19–25)

Hieronimo supposes he is reasoning for himself, but Revenge pulls the wires; and Revenge has only one basic pattern. If a man accepts his emotional appeal, he must trudge his paths. And the danger of this appeal is very great when one is suffering the loss of a loved one. "*Vindicta Mihi*" is then very easily swept aside as a most unsatisfying alternative that provides no active outlet for passion.

From our vantage point in the audience, however, we must not forget that the first four lines of the soliloquy, offering Christian-Stoic patience as an alternative to revenge, have really been answered only in emotional terms and not at all in moral terms. Morally there is an hiatus between line 5 and the remainder of the speech, try as we will to ignore it if we wish to "justify" Hieronimo. But on the other hand, we are not invited to condemn Hieronimo. *The Spanish Tragedy* is not a morality play but a tragedy, in which we witness an imaginative vision of "What 'tis to be subject to destiny" (III.xv.28). We are given an understanding of the workings of the heart and mind when love is killed, and Kyd is showing how the painful void left by that loss is filled with the passions of revenge. Surely Hieronimo remains a sympathetic character no matter how much he may echo and imitate Lorenzo or Revenge. Lorenzo had no honest basis for revenge: the void in his heart is an expression of the satanism of his nature. Hieronimo is pathetic even in his false pretenses, and he always makes us feel the power of the passion that drives him on. We see Lorenzo as one who consciously and inhumanly decries emotion and enjoys cruel hypocrisies. There remains between the two all the difference that separates a tragic figure from a villain.

When Hieronimo is interrupted by a group of four petitioners who ask him to plead for them in legal actions, we feel with him the bitter irony that he should be called upon to seek justice for others after seeing it fail in his own case. The petitioners unwittingly rub salt in his wounds by saying that no other advocate in Spain "will take half the pain/That he will, in pursuit of equity" (53–54). The cases of the first three men are ordinary suits of debt and the like, and Hieronimo at first accepts their papers with little ado. Bazulto, the fourth man, stands apart; he is so old that Hieronimo addresses him as "father" even before he knows that the murder of a son has caused his grief (67–85). Kyd builds very artfully to the climax of Hieronimo's recognition of himself in Bazulto. The mournful posture of the old man, with eyes and hands raised to heaven, should be staged in a way that immediately reminds us of Hieronimo. Bazulto's muteness, his inability to let his "woes/Give way unto my most distressful words," follows Hieronimo's inability to communicate with others and echoes one of his lines: "My grief no heart, my thoughts no tongue can tell" (III.ii.67).

But as I showed in Chapter II, although he recognizes his own cause and emotion in this old man, Hieronimo still does not fully see *himself* in him. A "lively portrait" suggests an essentially lifeless image that is somehow made active: the *man* is reduced to a portrait that is merely given the attribute of livingness (85). However, in its context the "lively" is paired with "my dying self." The *life* is only that of "O life, no life, but lively form of death" (III.ii.2). Hieronimo thus sees that "all as one are our extremities" (92), and he shares his possessions with Bazulto, yet he cannot respond to Bazulto's request for justice because he sees him in part as a derivative and inferior form of his own reality that is relatively unimportant in itself and that serves first of all to torture him for his failure so far to smite his enemies:

> If love's effects so strives in lesser things,
> If love enforce such moods in meaner wits,
> If love express such power in poor estates:
> Hieronimo, whenas a raging sea,
> Toss'd with the wind and tide, o'erturneth . . .
>   (III.xiii.99–103)

The image of the storm of passion signals Hieronimo's loss of self-control; for the rest of the scene he is engulfed in a whirlwind

of madness. At the beginning of the scene he had calmed himself
and tried to be reasonable, but now all his composure is shattered.
He has cried "See, see, O see" and looked deeply into an horrific
image (95). The experience has blinded him to the realities
around him. He denies justice to the petitioners by tearing their
papers, under the delusion that they are the limbs of his enemies
(121–23). At first he saw himself in Bazulto, but having been
driven mad by what he saw, he evades this identification; and he
next sees Horatio and then a fury from hell in the old man (133,
153). If he is oblivious to the realities around him, he sees the
underworld clearly and well (108–21). Like Andrea before him,
he will make the dark journey of the spirit to hell where, exactly
like Andrea, he will see Proserpina grant "Revenge" (121). Andrea's spirit made this journey only after death; indeed, he did
not begin to demand revenge until the end of Act I, and his experience of a growing possession by Revenge after death parallels
the growing passion of Hieronimo, whose tragedy it is to make
the spiritual journey through the land of the dead while he is still
alive: "O life, no life, but lively form of death."

Through his growing kinship with Andrea, Hieronimo is again
seeing *himself* in Bazulto when he sees him as Horatio seeking
justice and then as a fury sent from hell, since Horatio is by now
an alternate form of Andrea, and since Hieronimo is becoming a
form of the fury Revenge. But Bazulto wants him to come to the
level of being where Hieronimo is an agent of justice and he is a
poor petitioner for that justice (159–60). Bazulto's plea for justice
rings out in contrast against Hieronimo's immediately preceding
cry for vengeance (158). Hieronimo does not heed Bazulto's plea,
even though he is brought back closer to realities: "Thou art the
lively image of my grief" (162).

This second time that he sees Bazulto as his own lively image
Hieronimo expresses more real human sympathy than he had the
first time (161–75). He does not simply behold a lesser form of
his own grief but the "selfsame sorrow" (169). This time he really
looks at the old man, describing in detail what he sees and equating it with "my sorrows" (163). The scene ends on a note of quiet
pathos. Hieronimo's response to Bazulto has moved pathos before
in his mad wish to see his son in the old man and then in his
further identification with his son through seeing in him an
Horatio who has suddenly become older than his father (133,
150). But now for the first time the pathos of Bazulto's real situa-

tion is coming home to Hieronimo, and he truly pities him and
takes him as a guest to see Isabella. Although he still cannot
respond to Bazulto's need for justice, he can respond to his need
for sympathy. They dodder off together, the one helping the other
walk.

At this point our sympathy for Hieronimo has been worked up
to a high level. The cold-blooded Hieronimo of the earlier part
of the scene, who will use smiles to mask hatred, has given way
to a pathetic, pitying man. We have seen a lively image of grief,
and we feel that both Hieronimo and Bazulto have suffered more
than man can bear. We understand that Hieronimo has been
driven mad, and we are ready to give our sympathy if not our approval to anything he does.

Act III, Scene xiv

An immediate ironic contrast with the preceding scene is the
pair of happy fathers in scene xiv. The irony is not so much in the
contrast as in the fated sameness: at the end of the play the
Viceroy will be in much the same situation that Hieronimo has
just been in. Kyd emphasizes the joy and hope of the court in
order to make the reversal of the catastrophe as great as possible.
The King of Spain sees a lively image of himself in the Portuguese,
"For as we now are, so sometimes were these," and he and the
Viceroy will unite kingdoms, crowns, flesh, and all in the marriage
of Bel-imperia to Balthazar (III.xiv.6). The Viceroy himself wants
to go into isolation to thank heaven for the deliverance of his son
(32–38). The Viceroy is once again used by Kyd to present an
epitome of the tragic individual. The King speaks of his passion as
a "princely mood," an "extremity" of emotion that isolates the
Viceroy from other men as "nature strives" in awesome conflict
(35–38).

The Viceroy has no sooner gone off with the King than the
Duke turns to Lorenzo and questions him to see if he understands his relationship to others:

> Cast. She is thy sister?
> Lor.   Who, Bel-imperia?
> Ay, my gracious lord, and this is the day
> That I have long'd so happily to see.

    Cast. Thou wouldst be loath that any fault of thine
          Should intercept her in her happiness.
    Lor. Heavens will not let Lorenzo err so much.
                        (46–51)

The false piety of the last line masks Lorenzo's evil nature and
helps to define his isolation in the world of lies that his ego has
driven him to create. The falseness is particularly clear because we
can see Revenge as one who will not let Lorenzo err much longer.

  Lorenzo's false use of words introduces an emphasis on the
contrast between true and false words that continues through the
rest of the scene. Castile tells his son to "listen to my words," and
proceeds to speak truly that he has "heard it said" that Lorenzo
wrongs Hieronimo and blocks his suit to the King (52–58). He
reminds Lorenzo (and us) of Hieronimo's worth as a person and
of his former deeds of greatness, pointing out that dishonor will
result if Lorenzo is denounced by the old man (59–70). Then he
asks Lorenzo for the truth (71–84). Lorenzo has never been a
better actor than he is in this passage. He will perhaps be a finer
actor later in the play-within-the-play, but the foreign language
he speaks then will be no more difficult to interpret than his seem-
ingly plain talk here. The words of other people are false, he says;
people are "liberal of their tongues," in that they let themselves
say pretty much what they want to (74). Lorenzo is describing
his own falseness, but insists that he has been good to Hieronimo,
holding him off with "kind and courteous words" (82).

  The statement that those words were as free from malice to
Hieronimo as to Lorenzo's own soul is an ironic condemnation of
Lorenzo's soul, of course, since he spoke maliciously and not
kindly (83–84). The villain has reached that final state, just before the catastrophe, in which he tempts the fates to destroy him:
"Heavens will not let Lorenzo err so much" (51). When Lorenzo
sees that his father believes him, he presses his advantage by arguing that a man distracted in his mind by the death of his son may
be easily deluded: "Alas, how easy is it for him to err!" ([89]—
but heaven will not let *me* err). Lorenzo completes his conquest
of his father by proposing that Hieronimo and he should be pub-
licly reconciled.

  While Hieronimo is being sent for, Balthazar and Bel-imperia
enter and talk of *their* supposed reconciliation. The rest of the

scene is as much a series of play-acts as anything in the play-within-the-play could be: when there is falseness on both sides of a conflict, the world of hypocrisy and malice is only the distance of art away from the pretend world of tragedy. The people corrupt reality with false pretenses so long that, in the catastrophe, reality and false pretenses become inseparable.

Balthazar can never escape from the pretenses of his verbal artifices (95–106). Like Lorenzo and the Viceroy, he says heaven is taking care of things, though he still recognizes Bel-imperia's imperious being to be the "sovereign" of his happiness (96–97). He calls on her to let her sun-bright eyes shine on him. She, however, is saving the "new-kindled flame" of her eyes for the expression of hatred. Later, in the playlet, Balthazar-Soliman again asks Bel-imperia-Perseda to shine her gracious eyes on him, and she stabs him (III.xiv.99–103, IV.iv.55–60). Irony follows irony as Balthazar asks for a "truce," reminding us of the use of metaphors of war by Horatio and Bel-imperia shortly before the deadly implications of the metaphor became reality.

Following this little play of false artifice on one side and concealed hate on the other, the Duke innocently stage-manages an even more false scene between Hieronimo and Lorenzo. Kyd does very well at suggesting a great difference between the false friendship of Lorenzo and of Hieronimo. Lorenzo is as cool as ever, but Hieronimo is barely able to restrain his real feelings. Frantic with tension, the old man behaves very strangely at first; indeed, he seems to be on the brink of madness (117–29). "*Pocas palabras*": "few words": but, after a slow start, the words flow freely and falsely. Hieronimo hides his malice in his lamb's clothing (118), and he supposes all of the others also do so. How is he to distinguish Castile's true "Welcome Hieronimo" from the false ones of Balthazar and Lorenzo? (120–22). In very few words he expresses and conceals his feelings by ambiguously thanking them "for Horatio"—in his place or for his death (123). The Duke has begun by saying "I'll have a word with" Hieronimo, and now Hieronimo confines him to only one word by walking off after his introductory "this" (115, 125).

Finally, Hieronimo is made to understand that the Duke craves "a word" with him, and that this does not mean *a* word (128). Perhaps this helps him see that words are false and free. He joins the game with the others and outdoes them in his wildly exaggerated

ironies. Heaven forbid that Hieronimo should believe himself in-
jured by Lorenzo (139–49). They embrace, and Hieronimo continues to pour on the warm talk of friendship to the point where
we probably think Lorenzo and Balthazar should become suspicious, but they are completely deceived. Although they sense
that Hieronimo is distraught, they think it is only about Horatio's
murder, and they do not realize that he knows the murderers.
They are too false themselves to be able to sense his real feelings.

The Duke of Castile meanwhile believes that the reconciliation
has been sincere on both sides. When he invites Hieronimo to
keep him company for the day (165–66), Hieronimo accepts the
invitation, then stays behind to reveal to us how false his words
have been:

> Your lordship's to command.—Pha! keep your way.
> *Chi mi fa più carezze che non suole,*
> *Tradito mi ha, o tradir mi vuole.* (167–69)

"He who shows unaccustomed fondness for me has betrayed me
or wants to betray me" (Edwards' translation). As I argued in
Chapter II, Hieronimo defines here as evil not only Lorenzo's
but also his own conduct, for he has just shown unaccustomed
fondness in order to betray Lorenzo and Balthazar. The last betrayal is Hieronimo's inclusion of the Duke of Castile among those
whose friendship is evidence of malice, and his subsequent inclusion of him among his victims. Certainly Hieronimo's is one of
the most insane perversions of love into hate, that a person should
believe another to be hateful for the very reason that he acts in a
loving way.

Act III, Scene xv

Andrea, who still plays the part of the blindest person in the
audience, takes the betrothal of Balthazar and Bel-imperia and
the reconciliation of Lorenzo and Hieronimo to be real. The play
as a whole is a part of reality for Andrea (only *we* know it to be
play-acting), and therefore it is not surprising that he should also
take its various pretended scenes as real. It is important that the
failure of *revenge* up to this point in the action makes Andrea
question the prevalence of *love* in hell, whence he and Revenge

have come (III.xv.13–17). Such words remind us again of the cause of revenge: its tragic perversion of love into murderous hate.

Revenge says that his mood is "soliciting" the souls of the living, and he echoes Hieronimo in the idea that "in unquiet, quietness is feign'd,/And slumb'ring is a common worldly wile" (III.xv.24–25; cf. III.xiii.29–30). Andrea should not worry: Hieronimo is possessed with the spirit of Revenge; and, if he appears to be friendly with his enemies, that is the way Revenge works. Hieronimo and all the rest of the people are "subject to destiny" (III.xv.28). To reassure Andrea further, Revenge presents a dumbshow in which love itself destroys the hope of love; for Hymen, the god of marriage, *himself* extinguishes the torches that light the marriage of Bel-imperia and Balthazar (30–35). Ironically, this sign that Balthazar's love will be frustrated allows Andrea to relax with the thought that the "infernal powers" "will not tolerate a lover's woe" (37–38). Andrea cannot see Balthazar's life and death as a form of his own destiny.

CHAPTER 7

Hieronimo's Play

IN the dumbshow that concludes Act III, the god of marriage plays the part of one who quenches festive marriage torches in blood. This symbolic microcosm suggests the form of what is to follow: love will kill, and people will enact parts in a play that seem to reverse their true roles. From its first moments, Act IV is a culmination of all the play's transformations of love into hate. Bel-imperia says that Hieromino's shows of love for Horatio have been empty and that he is a "monstrous" and "unkind" (unnatural) father because he has not shown his love in the form of hate for Lorenzo and Balthazar (IV.i.7,18). She has been deceived, as the others have, by Hieronimo's appearance of friendship to his enemies; and it is deeply significant that it is *this* show of love that is really empty or "counterfeit" (cf. III. xiii. 20–24 and IV. i. 1–3). If Bel-imperia knew the malice Hieronimo feels, she would be reassured that he is a loving father, as she is a loving woman who "So lov'd his life, as still I wish their deaths" (22). It would never occur to her that the substitution of hate for love which she demands might itself be unnatural.

Bel-imperia thinks Hieronimo has forgotten to take revenge. At several points in the play it might appear that Hieronimo delays revenge, Hamlet-style, but there is no invitation to deep psychological analysis of the delay. Hieronimo, driven by the desire to destroy, is held back by the judge's inclination to proceed with caution. First he waits because he wants proof (III.ii–III.vii), then because he hopes for justice from the King (III.vii–III.xii). In Act III.xiii, he resolves to take revenge and is impatient with himself for having waited as long as he has; but in Act III.xiv we have seen him winning the confidence of Lorenzo and Balthazar in order to destroy them in the spectacular and dramatic manner that alone will satisfy his spectacular sense of loss. Now, in Act IV, he is ready to act.

Bel-imperia concludes her attack on Hieronimo's failure to act with a passionate vow that, if he does not take revenge, she will (23–29). Until this moment Hieronimo has been inclined to see Revenge for what the play defines it to be: a force sent from the underworld when the judges fail, a demonic urge that promises a perverse "joy amidst . . . discontent" (II.v.55, and cf. I.i.78–81, I.iv.16, I.v.5–9, III.ii.16–18, III.vii.9, III.xiii.108–13). Now, however, the support of Bel-imperia convinces him that heaven favors his revenge (IV.i.30–34). It would be a serious error to take this feeling as a statement that *Kyd* regards the revenge to be sanctioned by heaven, as certain critics have done. We must consider Hieronimo's statement that "the saints do sit soliciting/ For vengeance" in relation to Revenge's statement only about sixty lines earlier that *his* mood sits "soliciting their souls" for revenge (III.xv.20). Because of Hieronimo's pious sense of justice, he desperately needs to believe heaven is on his side; but Revenge's words must remind us to regard the belief with skepticism.

Hieronimo and Bel-imperia have just vowed to join one another in revenge when Lorenzo and Balthazar enter to ask Hieronimo to "help" them:

BAL.   How now, Hieronimo?
        What, courting Bel-imperia?
HIER.   Ay my lord,
        Such courting as, I promise you,
        She hath my heart, but you, my lord, have hers.
LOR.   But now, Hieronimo, or never,
        We are to entreat your help.
HIER.   My help?
        Why my good lords, assure yourselves of me,
        For you have given me cause,
        Ay, by my faith have you. (IV.i.52–60)

Balthazar's joking reference to Hieronimo's "courting" of Bel-imperia carries forward the theme of perverted love. Lover-like, Bel-imperia has promised to "join with" Hieronimo in love of and revenge for Horatio, just as earlier she and Horatio joined in love of and revenge for Andrea. Balthazar has Bel-imperia's heart only in the sense that he has twice destroyed her lovers. Lorenzo's request for help keeps Hieronimo on the course of cloaking malice in kindness. His emphasis on their having given him cause to "help" seems openly sarcastic to us, and we cannot help wondering whether Kyd has not sacrificed character to plot in making Lorenzo so guileless and unsuspecting as he is for the remainder of the play. Since the elimination of Serberine and Pedringano, Lorenzo has had a false sense of security; and it has encouraged him to accept the pretended friendship of Hieronimo and Bel-imperia as real. But, when Hieronimo now asks him and Balthazar to enact parts in a play in which they will be murdered by himself and Bel-imperia, should not Lorenzo be at least a *little* suspicious?

I think Kyd rather hoped we would not stop to ask this question, but perhaps it is not an entirely fair one. As I suggested in my discussion of Act III.xiv, Lorenzo has deceived others so much that he has come to deceive himself the most of all. He believes the story he told himself about his henchmen, and he probably has persuaded himself to believe the story he told Bel-imperia about Horatio's death and her imprisonment. In his fearful egotism, he wants to believe that his cleverness has won the friendship of Hieronimo and with it total security. His emotional need for security may make him believe he is secure in something of the same way Hieronimo's need to believe that heaven favors his revenge makes him think that it does.

To a certain degree Lorenzo *is* suspicious, or at any rate the less guileful Balthazar is:

> BAL. [*aside to* LORENZO.] How like you this?
> LOR. Why thus, my lord.
> We must resolve to soothe his humours up.
> (IV.i.190–92)

Perhaps Lorenzo sees the threat in the situation, but is convinced that he can easily forestall real danger because his mind is clear and Hieronimo's is sick. Or he may feel that the threat is a *distracted* malice that will work itself out harmlessly in the *pretended* murders of the playlet. Hieronimo should probably be acted in such a way that he seems insane enough to justify Lorenzo in the over-confident belief that he is safe.

Hieronimo's "courting" of Bel-imperia has reminded us of Horatio's courting of her in Act I.iii, and Balthazar strongly reminds us of Act I.iv when he asks Hieronimo to present a show for the wedding (IV.i.60–67). As I have remarked, the first and last acts are both, in different ways, microcosmic enactments of the whole play that mirror each other. Or, to use another metaphor that Elizabethan plays commonly apply to such a pattern, the wheel has come full circle from the beginning of the play to its ending. As is usual when there is such a pattern, the coming full circle is a reversal that fulfills the most ironic potential of the earlier action. Lorenzo and Balthazar were "actors in th' accursed tragedy" of Horatio's murder, so now they must be actors in their own tragedy (III.vii.41). All of the people have concealed an evil reality beneath pretense, so now pretense will become an evil reality for them in which earlier roles are reversed by Lorenzo's becoming Horatio and by Hieronimo's becoming Lorenzo.

In a different way from that in *Hamlet*, we see that an "act" is a complex thing. Hieronimo speaks of his play:

> Now would your lordships favour me so much
> As but to grace me with your acting it—
> I mean each one of you to play a part—
> Assure you it will prove most passing strange.
> (IV.i.81–84)

Hieronimo means that in the play he will make them enact in reality what they think is mere pretense, but he tries to conceal this idea by his hasty explanation that he means only for each of them to *play*-act a part. Several confusions of pretense and reality are important in the tragedies of Lorenzo and Hieronimo. In different ways each of them play-acts so well that he gets carried away in the fictions he has created and therefore loses sight of the relation between pretense and reality.

Hieronimo knows that the pretense is real in its destruction of Lorenzo and Balthazar, but he does not see that, if that much of the play is real, there may be a meaningful relation between the role he acts in the playlet and the role he acts in the play as a whole. When he assigns the parts he says "I'll play the murderer, I warrant you,/For I already have conceited that" (133–134). In playing the murderer as a mask for his revenge, and especially considering that he will murder Erastus, the character in the playlet who corresponds to Horatio, Hieronimo unintentionally perverts his cause and shows that a revenge is in "act" a murder. Both Hieronimo and Lorenzo see some of the implications of using pretense as reality, but they are so much concerned with the new shape they want to give reality through pretense that they are blinded to the psychological effects and imaginative implications of the metamorphoses of reality that they achieve. Hieronimo has "conceited" or imagined playing the murderer with such intensity that he can no longer separate his mind from that role and its horrors.

Balthazar and Lorenzo agree to act in Hieronimo's play before he tells them the story. With his usual perversity, Lorenzo responds "O excellent!" when he hears the tale of treacherous murders (127). Balthazar waits to find out who is to play what part before he reacts; then he says he thinks a comedy would be better (155). Once again we see that, when his passion of love is not overwhelming him, Balthazar is a reasonably sane person whose common sense contrasts effectively with the perverse and murderous desires of the others. There is a fine plaintive quality to his idea that a comedy would be more appropriate to his wedding celebration than a tragedy would be. When Hieronimo argues in reply that a tragedy is appropriate to the kingly audience, he does not comment on its appropriateness to a wedding because, to him, the occasion is not a wedding but a royally spectacular revenge (156–66).

Hieronimo insists that the script be spoken in foreign languages. He may have hinted at this requirement when he said his play had been written to be performed "By gentlemen and scholars too,/Such as could tell what to speak" (102–3). Balthazar is to speak in Latin, Hieronimo in Greek, Lorenzo in Italian, and Bel-imperia in French. As a result, each character will be isolated from the others within a language that he alone speaks, as they have been isolated by false use of language all along (175–78). Hieronimo has a two-fold purpose in having the play be impossible for the audience to understand. First, he wants to follow it with an oration in which he will explain "the play"— his play and Kyd's—by telling all about the murder of Horatio and even producing his mangled corpse on the stage (182–87). Second, Hieronimo uses the several foreign languages as a dramatic symbol of the meaning of his revenge as the fall of Babel or Babylon-Spain: "Now shall I see the fall of Babylon,/Wrought by the heavens in this confusion" (195–96).

By imagining Spain to be Babylon and by making the villains of his playlet be Turks, Hieronimo reinforces his earlier idea that heaven is at work in his revenge (cf. 196, 32). This conception of his action enables him to play the murderer in such an extremely self-righteous spirit that he thinks he is justified to include the Duke of Castile among his victims. He has imagined and then convinced himself that he is God's agent for the punishment of a whole nation, so there is no need for him to distinguish between the innocent and the guilty.

Act IV, Scene ii

Scene ii is one of those showing that the essence of revenge may be suicide. The pain of the loss of a loved person is so great that the survivor wishes to be dead himself. The masculine, aggressive way to seek death is in a retaliation for the loss that is so contrived that there is no way for the revenger to escape death. This is the way of Hieronimo in murdering his enemies in full sight of the King and in the midst of the court with all its armed attendants.

The present scene enacts the feminine counterpart to Hieronimo's course of action. Helpless to destroy those who took her son's life, Isabella takes her revenge against the sources of life in the arbor and herself. The logic of her revenge is like Hieronimo's: homicide is monstrous and must therefore not be tolerated. The King has refused justice, therefore "I will revenge myself upon" not my enemies but "this place/Where thus they murder'd my beloved son./ *She cuts down the arbour*" (1–5). "*Thus* they murder'd": Isabella imagines herself to be symbolically striking back at the murderers and at the same time re-enacting their crime. This action is her equivalent of Hieronimo's killing Lorenzo at a moment when Lorenzo is in the position of Horatio.

As Isabella slashes down the boughs, she cries out against the tree as "unfortunate and fatal," possibly suggesting a connection between the corruption of Spain and the fall of man in Eden because of such a tree (IV.ii.7).[1] "Rent them up," wails Isabella, and Edwards' footnote reminds us that "rent" has earlier been used in this sense by Hieronimo when he tore the legal papers of his clients under the delusion that he was tearing the limbs of enemies (III.xiii.122,IV.ii.8). Hieronimo is an agent of justice as a Marshal of Spain, and his mad impulse for revenge makes him pervert this role by destroying the means of justice. Isabella is a mother, and her mad impulse for revenge makes her destroy the arbor not only as a hateful place but as a symbol of herself as a mother: "Fruitless for ever may this garden be,/Barren the earth . . ." (14–15). Then, having first committed symbolic suicide as a mother, she really kills herself as mother in revenge for her son (25), using the same weapon and pronouncing the same curse that she had for the arbor:

> And as I curse this tree from further fruit,
> So shall my womb be cursed for his sake,
> And with this weapon will I wound the breast,
> > *She stabs herself.*
> The hapless breast, that gave Horatio suck.
> > (35–38)

Just before killing herself Isabella complains that Hieronimo shamefully delays his revenge. Revenge is a dreadful undertaking, and one function of this scene, as of Bel-imperia's pleadings in the scene before, is to whip Hieronimo and the audience into an emotional frenzy in which the deed will finally come as a release. Kyd heightens the effect of the urgings of Bel-imperia and Isabella by having them both be deceived by Hieronimo's apparent peace with Lorenzo and Balthazar. Their fear of this peace gives a tone of urgency and despair to their voices. Isabella's hopelessness is nowhere expressed more powerfully than in the line "And none but I bestir me—to no end" (34). In her madness she has a compulsion to "bestir" herself, but her acts can only be fruitless and barren, leading "to no end." To Isabella, life has become a round of futile activity; and in her despair she has arrived at the life-denying *no*-end of suicide.

Act IV, Scene iii

In the brief scene iii Kyd uses the hustle and bustle of Hieronimo's preparations for the play to build up suspense. Hieronimo is again friendly to the Duke of Castile while hating him in his heart. After the Duke and then Balthazar leave the stage, Hieronimo recapitulates his motives for revenge in order to screw his courage and our understanding to the sticking point. He adds

to the murder of Horatio the suicide of Isabella, "Once his
mother and thy dearest wife" (25). *Once* she was these things,
but now the love of these relationships is lost forever and so is
redeemable only in the hate of murderers, "For nothing wants
but acting of revenge" (30).

It is not possible to be sure how the play-within-the-play was
staged in Elizabethan times. The staging is of particular importance here because it has a bearing on the interpretation of what
occurs after the playlet when Hieronimo explains what has happened, the attendants seize him, and then the King and the
others ask him to explain his actions as though they have not
heard him. Philip Edwards argues for the majority of scholars
that the play's royal audience took its place on the stage with
the actors of the playlet. This may have been the case, but I
think the evidence favors placing the audience in a gallery over
the stage. Hieronimo says to Castile: "Let me entreat your grace,/
That when the train are pass'd into the gallery/You would vouch-
safe to throw me down the key" (11–13). Most early usage implies
that the word "gallery" in an Elizabethan theater would refer to
the balcony-like area above the stage. Moreover, the phrasing of
Hieronimo's reference to the gallery seems to imply that it is some
other place than where he is standing. He does not ask that
Castile should *give* him the key when the royal train *comes*,
but that he should *throw* him *down* the key, as from above,
when they have *passed* into *the* gallery, as into a place requiring
specification. The idea that Castile is to throw down the key
from a stage gallery seems more likely to me than Edwards' idea
that Hieronimo wants him to "throw the key down [on the floor]
for me."

Edwards believes that this explanation, however unlikely it
may seem, must be accepted because other evidence proves that
the royal train is on the stage with Hieronimo. One thing Edwards cites is Hieronimo's request of Balthazar that he "Bring
a chair and a cushion for the king," which is followed by the
stage direction *"Enter Balthazar with a chair"* (16). It may be
that this chair is brought on the stage for the purpose of seating
the Spanish King during the playlet, but again I think there are
other meanings that are at least as probable as Edwards' reading
of Hieronimo's request that the key be thrown down. The stage
direction does not say where Balthazar puts the chair. True, it

does not say *"Enter above,"* but on at least two other occasions a stage direction may have neglected to indicate *"above"* when it was applicable (II.ii.6,III.ix.14). The implication of Hieronimo's *"Bring,"* however, is that the chair and cushion should be brought to Hieronimo on the stage.

The possibility still remains that the king who is to use the chair and cushion is the king in the play, the emperor Soliman, who is to be played by Balthazar. The word "king" is used elsewhere in the play for "Viceroy," and it seems reasonable to suppose that it might be used loosely to refer to an emperor. If the chair and cushion are for the real King of Spain, why is Balthazar and not an ordinary attendant responsible for them? How are we to suppose that such things have been managed in other scenes? The King is to have a chair and a cushion: are the Viceroy and Duke going to stand during the playlet? In this scene Hieronimo's other actions and his directions and queries to Balthazar have to do with the playlet; does it not make sense that this one does too, and that Hieronimo is asking Balthazar to bring the chair that is to be his own throne in the playlet?

Act IV, Scene iv

The opening stage direction for scene iv is simply *"Enter Spanish King, Viceroy, the Duke of Castile, and their train,"* with no mention of entering *"above,"* i.e., into a gallery or balcony, although I think the dialogue in Act IV.iii implies that Kyd meant them to be seated there above the action, slightly removed from the scene. There is additional evidence later in this scene that they are not on the stage with Hieronimo. When Hieronimo runs to hang himself, the Viceroy calls out "Break ope the doors, run, save Hieronimo!" (156). If the Viceroy and the King were on the stage with the "train" of attendants mentioned in the stage direction for their entry at the start of the scene, why should it be necessary for anyone to break doors down to get at Hieronimo? The attendants could simply step forward and seize him. Indeed, Hieronimo probably wanted the key to the gallery so that the King's attendants could not easily interfere with any part of his show, from the murders in the playlet through his harangue to his suicide.

In Act IV.iii, Hieronimo gave the Duke a copy of the playlet with its "argument" or plot, and now the royal party uses it to follow the action, which the actors supposedly perform in Latin, Greek, Italian, and French. The printed text of the play gives the playlet in English, and it is possible that the playlet was actually performed in English with the audience to understand that it should imagine the foreign languages. At the end of his murderous playlet Hieronimo explains that it was his revenge for the murder of Horatio. He displays his son's body and summarizes the action of the play from the love of Bel-imperia and Horatio onward. After about seventy-five lines of explanation he concludes with "Urge no more words, I have no more to say," and then *"He runs to hang himself"* (152).

The members of the royal audience gather that their children have been killed, but they have somehow missed or misunderstood Hieronimo's explanation since they ask him why he killed and who his confederates were (163–67, 176). A number of scholars have felt that there is a serious textual problem here, that by error alternative passages have been printed side by side as though they belong together.[2] These scholars think we must choose between Hieronimo's lengthy explanation and the matter that follows, in which the royal party questions him and he finally goes so far as to bite out his tongue rather than break a mysterious vow not to betray his confederates (187–91).

None of the later Elizabethan editions of the play entirely solve this problem. This lack would ordinarily not be strange, since later editions often copied earlier ones; but in 1602 an edition of this play appeared with a number of additions to the text, including a passage in the midst of this supposed confusion that retains the royal party's questions, although it deletes Hieronimo's specific refusal to tell who his confederates were. He simply does not answer the question at all. From the deletion of Hieronimo's refusal to violate a vow that we have never heard of earlier, we can see that the reviser was concerned with clearing up what he took to be inconsistencies in the play, and I think that it is therefore likely that he saw nothing inconsistent in having the royal party ask why he has killed—a question Hieronimo has just answered.[3]

It seems to me that Kyd wanted his climax to stress the powerlessness of the tongue, and when the moment came he simply invented the vow as a reason for Hieronimo not to speak, without any preparation for it at all. But perhaps we can explain all of the original text of 1592 as it stands, and I certainly think we can explain Hieronimo's general reluctance to talk and the royal party's questions asked in spite of his earlier full explanation. The idea that he will refuse to talk later is implicit in the last line of his oration after the playlet: "Urge no more words, I have no more to say" (152). This statement establishes a link between Hieronimo's explanation and his subsequent refusal to explain, although it does nothing to account for the change. What we want are logical, psychological, and thematic explanations for his refusal to talk and for the fact that the others seem to have heard very little of what he has said in his long oration. The only thing to do is to review the sequence of events and the alternative interpretations in greater detail.

At the end of Hieronimo's long oration, the King and the others know that Lorenzo and Balthazar have been murdered; but the Viceroy promises Hieronimo that he will be spared if he will "but inform the king of these events," and the King cries "Speak, traitor: damned, bloody murderer, speak!" and calls the murders "undeserving" (157, 163, 165). If we assume that they have heard Hieronimo's story, the only natural explanation for their questions is that they do not believe or cannot accept what he has said. The Viceroy, for one, has certainly learned not to believe every story he is told; and the King's accusation of treason is a way of saying that he thinks there is more to what Hieronimo has done than he has been willing to tell. The Viceroy's promise of protection for Hieronimo may indicate that he thinks the old man can be humored into talking. After all, they might well think Hieronimo has acted in madness. And in addition to possible suspicions of Hieronimo's treason or madness, there is in that royal chorus of "why? why? why?" a note of sheer agony. Even after all has been explained, the parents can never understand why so horrible a thing should have happened.

And well they might ask, because we know that Hieronimo's explanation has *not* been complete. He is not aware that behind all the action stands the figure of Revenge; he has not even been able to explain that Andrea is involved in the original cause for his revenge (98–107). Hieronimo does not fully understand *The Spanish Tragedy* and the King does not understand either *The Tragedy of Soliman and Perseda* or the "show" of Horatio's body and Hieronimo's "play" of explanation that has followed it (89,

151). As typically in this play, members of an audience mistake the reality of their relation to shows that are presented to them. Often they do not understand because they do not see what is happening in the show as a part of their reality, or they only partly understand how it is real. At the end of every act we have seen that Andrea cannot understand the play, and in Act I.iv, the Spanish King could not understand Hieronimo's dumbshow.

As I have also noted earlier, people of high station think themselves to be above the action of those around them, and they try to act as puppeteers or as an audience having little human responsibility or concern for what is going on among *others* who are *lower* than themselves and not *forms* of themselves. So here Hieronimo knows that his play is real as a vehicle for revenge, but as puppeteer he fails to see the significance of putting himself as a puppet in the place of Lorenzo, the murderer. The King, the Duke, and the Viceroy watch the bloody realities of the play (I would seat them *above,* in a gallery) with no human concern, jesting about deaths they assume are occurring at a puppet level of reality lower than their own (70–71). Then Hieronimo tells them that they are on the same level of reality as the playlet, and they force open the doors to join the action on Hieronimo's level.

But they still cannot accept Hieronimo's explanation. Even if they were to believe that he has not lied or acted madly, perhaps they cannot accept the murder of three persons of royal blood in revenge for the murder of a mere nobleman's son. We must note that Hieronimo does *not* entirely fail to answer their "why? why? why?" His first words in response stress the idea that he is on their level of reality, that he has feelings just like theirs (168–70). Does not his introductory exclamation of "O good words!" suggest his despair of the power of his earlier words to explain, as well as his feeling that what the King and the others have said has been empty? They literally could not understand the words of the playlet because it was spoken in a babble of foreign languages, but the failure of words to communicate has been an important theme of the play all along that is now crystallizing in the playlet, in the King's inability to understand Hieronimo, and finally in Hieronimo's gesture of biting out his tongue.

To recapitulate the argument to this point: Hieronimo explains the story of revenge as far as he knows it, and then wishes to escape all further need to speak by killing himself (152–53). The King and the others cannot accept his story for several reasons: (1) there is possibly the suspicion that this strange device of murders in a play is a sign that Hieronimo's story and his deeds are not rational; (2) there is a suspicion that Hieronimo is a traitor and has not told the truth; (3) underlying both these suspicions, there is the inability to comprehend and to bear the reality of so sudden and so terrible a loss—*Why* did this have to happen?—and (4) "shows" are inexplicable to audiences who think they are *entirely* above the action.

So far, then, there are not necessarily any textual problems. The royal party has questions about Hieronimo's story, and he tries to answer them (to l. 175). But there is another question: "who were thy confederates in this?" (176). This question and this one alone Hieronimo refuses to answer, biting out his tongue and killing himself instead: "never shalt thou force me to reveal/ The thing which I have vow'd inviolate" (187–88). This seems to us a strange thing for Hieronimo to say. Maybe we should solve our problem about the text by agreeing to regard Hieronimo's strange replies, together with the biting out of his tongue, as signs of his insanity. We know of no confederates who have helped Hieronimo, except Bel-imperia, and the Viceroy himself immediately offers her name in answer to the question (177–79). Hieronimo promised to protect the Hangman who brought him the letter from Pedringano to Lorenzo, but that hardly makes the Hangman Hieronimo's confederate; and we have no knowledge of any vow of silence in connection with the Hangman or any other person. In his oration Hieronimo made it clear that Bel-imperia has been his co-revenger, although he did not tell about her letter or their mutual vow of revenge. He simply says that she was appointed to the part of Perseda so she could kill Balthazar, who had offended her (135–39), and that she was not following his plan when she killed herself (140–45). So maybe we are to understand that he has vowed not to reveal the extent of her involvement in the plot, or that he has had some other confederate, perhaps a servant who has had no lines but has become a witness, at least, if not an active confederate.

In any case, even if we cannot understand what vow Hieronimo refers to, the question about confederates is not an un-

reasonable one—except perhaps to critical ears that know the
whole story backward and forward anyway. We must imagine
the Duke of Castile staring at the bodies of his son and daughter
lying dead before him. How well could he concentrate on a long
story told by a half-mad old man? If he heard that his daughter
was a confederate in the murder of her brother, his only son,
would he not still ask "why?" and, desperately, "who were thy
confederates in this?" Probably there is more emotional logic
than narrative logic in the questions asked by the royal party.
There is surely more emotion than sense in their desire to torture Hieronimo: they may be well aware there is no more to say.
Like Hieronimo, they really care very little about words. They
ask for them, but only to have an excuse to exact emotional
satisfaction by inflicting pain, in short, to take revenge:

> KING. And if in this he satisfy us not,
>   We will devise th'extremest kind of death
>   That ever was invented for a wretch.
>   (196–98)

I am not at all certain that my explanation of the apparent
inconsistencies is correct, but I hope I have shown that the scene
can be acted and made meaningful as it stands. One simple way
to stage the scene that would be natural and that would follow
much of the interpretation I have offered would be to have the
royal party so shocked and grief-stricken that it does not pay
close attention to most of what Hieronimo says in his long
speech. Instead the members of the party might turn to each
other in horror and then begin to push their way from the gallery toward the stage to reach the bodies and Hieronimo. In the
last part of the scene, Hieronimo's strange lines about secret
vows and so on should almost certainly be accompanied by other
signs that he is mad, if only to prepare the audience for his
biting out his tongue.

With the supposed inconsistencies and the action of the scene
somewhat clarified, we can consider the play-within-the-play
and Hieronimo's explanation of his revenge. I have already discussed the many ways in which the playlet is important, and it
must suffice here to draw these together and summarize them.
The playlet is at once a re-enactment of a past murder and an

enactment of new murders that are the result of the first one. In this way it suggests the fundamental identity of murder and revenge, a suggestion that is obviously manifested in having the chief revenger play the part of a murderer. As a microcosm of the whole *Spanish Tragedy,* the playlet recapitulates the play's concern for the way love may drive men to deeds of hate. Soliman-Balthazar loves both Perseda-Bel-imperia and Erastus-Horatio-(Lorenzo), but the imperiousness of beauty conquers his love of Erastus and makes him kill him: *"Why, let him die, so love commandeth me"* (48). In response to the murder of Erastus-Horatio, Perseda-Bel-imperia kills Soliman-Balthazar because love commands her. Then, also at the command of love, she joins pretense and reality forever by killing herself. As Revenge originally promised Andrea, she has slain Balthazar; and she has done so as an act of revenge both in pretense and in reality. The roles of Bel-imperia and Balthazar in the playlet are what they are in the play because at the end of the play they are still the people they were at the beginning—he, a killer of her lover; she, a woman whose lover has been murdered.

The roles of Hieronimo and Lorenzo, however, are not the same at beginning and end of the play. Lorenzo was the enemy of Balthazar and the ally of Horatio in the battle, and the action has made him the friend of Balthazar and the murderer of Horatio. In the playlet, therefore, he plays a new role and is killed in the place of Horatio, his own victim: murder is suicide. At the beginning of the play, Hieronimo was an agent of justice, but now he has become a hate-filled agent of private revenge. In the playlet we see that he is pleased to enact the part of the ruthless killer: revenge is murder (and implies suicide, as we have seen).

As a microcosm of the whole *Spanish Tragedy,* the playlet is its greatest scene of imprisonment and tragic isolation. However the symbol of the locked door may literally work, Hieronimo's purpose is to keep the forces of the outside world and of higher authority from interfering with his play, his explanation, or his suicide. It is part of Hieronimo's tragic delusion that his authority governs events, that he is author as well as actor in his own tragedy (147).

But, despite his explanation of the playlet that he has imagined and written, he does not know that Revenge has shaped events, that forces are working which no locked door can hold off. It is Hieronimo's idea to free his will of outside influence; but, in escaping into a world of make-believe where he can transform reality to suit his own will, he becomes trapped, as Lorenzo also becomes trapped, in his own fictions. We need only remind ourselves that Hieronimo symbolically casts himself as murderer of his own son to see that he has not really understood his playlet. Even if he has inscribed it on paper, he is not truly its author in the sense he thinks he is.

Every man is isolated within his own passions and character, separated from others by barriers stronger than locked doors or differences of language. Like the royal audience to the playlet, men cannot see outside their own individual positions in the hierarchies of personality and society well enough to understand that those who appear to be at an inferior level are forms of themselves. Their children die before their eyes without their realizing what is happening. More tragic still, even the man who knows that the action of the playlet is real for his victims does not enter fully enough into Lorenzo's place (or his own) to see that he has become a form of Lorenzo as a guileful, dissembling murderer. If Hieronimo could see this ultimate identity of himself with others, he might be capable of justice instead of murdering another father, the Duke of Castile.

But Hieronimo's blindness always remains tragic. He never becomes a villain, for the great strength of his feelings makes us sympathize with his deeds at the same time that we see them as flawed. Hieronimo's long speech in explanation of his play is more than anything else a release of the passionate grief he has forced himself to restrain while preparing for this moment. The artificial tones of the play-within-the-play rendered his feelings only very weakly, and Hieronimo's show of shows is really the body of his dead son:

> See here my show, look on this spectacle:
> Here lay my hope, and here my hope hath end:
> Here lay my heart, and here my heart was slain:
> Here lay my treasure, here my treasure lost:
> Here lay my bliss, and here my bliss bereft:
> But hope, heart, treasure, joy and bliss,
> All fled, fail'd, died, yea, all decay'd with this.

From forth these wounds came breath that gave me life;
They murder'd me that made these fatal marks.

(89–97)

He goes on to force himself to relive the murder of his son:

. . . merciless they butcher'd up my boy,
In black dark night, to pale dim cruel death.
He shrieks, I heard, and yet methinks I hear,
His dismal outcry echo in the air:
With soonest speed I hasted to the noise,
Where hanging on a tree I found my son,
Through-girt with wounds, and slaughter'd as you see.
And griev'd I, think you, at this spectacle?
Speak, Portuguese, whose loss resembles mine:
If thou canst weep upon thy Balthazar,
'Tis like I wail'd for my Horatio. (106–16)

At the end of the scene the Viceroy and the King do grieve for
Balthazar and the others. The King's vision remains more than
narrowly personal, perhaps because he is not touched quite so
nearly as the Viceroy, and he is able to see the doom of "the
whole succeeding hope" of Spain in the many deaths (203). The
Viceroy, however, has lost his only son, and the action of the
play ends with his final tragic echo of Hieronimo's entirely personal agony and desire to die in the death of his son:

Take up our hapless son, untimely slain:
Set me with him, and he with woeful me,
Upon the mainmast of a ship unmann'd,
And let the wind and tide haul me along
To Scylla's barking and untamed gulf,
Or to the loathsome pool of Acheron,
To weep my want for my sweet Balthazar.

(210–16)

Act IV, Scene v

Andrea, like Hieronimo in scene iv, exults in scene v in "blood
and sorrow" that "finish my desires" (IV.v.2). He accepts all the
suffering of the play—that of his friends as well as his enemies
—as "spectacles to please my soul" (12). Now he wants to return
to Proserpina, the Queen of the Underworld, to beg her to take
care of his friends "in pleasing sort" and to take revenge against

his foes (13–16). Revenge replies that he will personally take the
foes to the tortures of "deepest hell" (27). Revenge is obviously
carried away with himself as a master puppeteer, and perhaps
we are to see that he has deluded himself into thinking he is the
supreme power in hell.

Actually, in Act I.i it was indicated that he is only a puppet
of Proserpina who is called in when Minos and the other judges
of the underworld cannot reach a decision about a dead man's
fate (I.i.33–89). Revenge's assumption of authority in the final
chorus encourages Andrea, in turn, to think of himself as judge
of his enemies instead of as one who will *beg* Proserpina for a
judgment in his favor (cf. IV.v.13 and 30). This change in Andrea
provides a last instance of the growth of the revenge spirit from
begging for judgment of a higher authority to a usurpation of
judgment in which one person urges another on: first Revenge
and Andrea in Act I.i, then Horatio and Bel-imperia, then
Lorenzo and Balthazar, then Hieronimo and Bel-imperia, and
now the wheel has come full circle back to Revenge and Andrea.
We may deduce from this pattern that we are to see the rewards
and punishments meted out here as expressions of the character
and experience of Andrea and Revenge, and not simply as the
play's final judgments. We do not feel that Kyd wants us to
reject the punishments Andrea calls down on Balthazar and the
others, for we share his sympathy for Hieronimo and much of
his hate of Lorenzo; but perhaps we may be repelled somewhat
by the terrors invoked and by the satanic anticipation of Andrea,
whose soul is at last the complete prisoner of Revenge (30–44).

The ghastly punishments are, of course, revenges; and they are
therefore just chiefly in terms of the emotional demands of the
situation. Hieronimo has performed deeds almost as horrible,
devious, and unjust as Lorenzo's, yet we assign him to peace in
the afterlife because he comes to evil tragically and in the process
of seeking to escape and destroy evil when his passions overwhelm his reason and he is possessed by a power greater than
himself. Lorenzo, on the other hand, is a man of unredeemed
evil. He embraces villainy consciously and is motivated by egotistical desires to use others for his own pleasure. Lorenzo is an
active and conscious agent of evil; Hieronimo is a tragic victim
of passion and evil. The conflict between these two types of men
was to become central in many of the greatest Elizabethan
tragedies.

CHAPTER 8

Hieronimo Is Mad Again

*T*HE SPANISH TRAGEDY really came into its own more in the triumphs of its offspring than its own success. For all Kyd's genius of imaginative conception, construction, and dramatic characterization, it is likely that the play's excesses of action and language will always keep it from being regarded as a truly great work. There are scenes of effective poetic action, but sometimes we find the language and the plot too violent, artificial, or mechanical for greatness. Oh, we cry, if only Kyd had been able to write great poetry! And so we turn again to Shakespeare and to other writers who sometimes built on Kyd's conceptions.

Much has been written about the influence of Kyd and Shakespeare on the other writers of revenge tragedy, especially on John Marston, Henry Chettle, Cyril Tourneur, Beaumont and Fletcher, John Webster, Thomas Middleton, John Ford, and James Shirley.[1] It is important to observe that our general impression of these other writers is closer to our impression of Kyd than of Shakespeare. This is true partly because Shakespeare is incomparably the greatest dramatic poet of his era, and partly because his work is rather different in outlook and tone from the other major Elizabethan tragic writing. Shakespeare's plays make us feel the greatness and beauty of tragic man even at his worst; and, although we may also be made to know man's folly as something inescapable and dreadful, there is not that degree of contempt for man that we sometimes feel in the anonymous *Revenger's Tragedy,* for instance, or in Webster's *White Devil.* From Marlowe through Middleton, the other writers frequently depict tragic man as the devil's or Fortune's fool, stressing the absurdity of tragic fate much more than its pathos or its grandeur. In these plays man is often treated as a mad puppet taking part in a lurid melodrama. Like Pedringano, he dances in his cords with the grotesque and horrible gestures of a hanged man kicking in his death spasm. He is a creature whom it is appropriate to subject to the most fantastic ironies imaginable, and only at his greatest moments is he to be understood sympathetically as a unique, suffering individual.

In *The Spanish Tragedy* Kyd found the forms that were to be the prototypes for the most important single line of development in the later drama, the fusion of tragic action and comic plot in the tragedy of intrigue. Within this new tragic form Kyd showed how to weave separate actions into a single plot of great complexity that provided so many opportunities for reversals that the ironies can easily become ludicrous and many scenes can come close to the manner of situation comedy. The tendency toward ironic situation comedy within tragedy became particularly pronounced in such plays as *The Revenger's Tragedy*, the tragedies of Beaumont and Fletcher, Middleton's *Women Beware Women*, and Shirley's *The Traitor* and *The Cardinal*. The tendency can also be felt, though not so strongly, in *Othello*, and in *Hamlet*, where it is the *sport* to have the engineer hoist with his own petard.

Most of the developments of bizarre irony in later intrigue tragedy are at least latent in Kyd's play. One of the most sophisticated kinds of irony in later plays grows out of Kyd's scenes that enact with grim twists the clichés of romantic literature. The most obvious of these scenes in *The Spanish Tragedy* is the one in which the conceit that sexual consummation is a "death" is suddenly transformed into the literal death of a lover. More subtle is Bel-imperia's use of Horatio's love for her as part of her revenge against Balthazar, Kyd's sidelong glance at the convention that in order to test the love of a man who woos her, a lady may ask him to kill someone. The twisted enactments of conceits and conventions become especially notable in such plays as Beaumont and Fletcher's *Maid's Tragedy* and Thomas Middleton and William Rowley's *The Changeling*. In both these plays, for example, there is a new twist on the idea of the lady asking her would-be lover to slay a man. In *The Maid's Tragedy* he finds that he is to kill *himself;* in *The Changeling* the lady does not realize the implication of her request, and finds that she has put herself in the power of an unwanted lover when he has done the deed for her.

The possibilities of the tragedy of intrigue were, of course, most greatly realized in *Hamlet*, which Shakespeare based on a lost play that Kyd may very well have written. Of the many relationships between *The Spanish Tragedy* and *Hamlet* that point up Kyd's general influence on later drama, we might mention the play-within-the-play, the "mad," dissembling revenger, the Senecan philosophical soliloquies, and the highly theatrical presentation of exciting, spectacular, and horrible events only described in Senecan tragedy. In *The Revenger's Tragedy* and other plays that followed *Hamlet*, the willful and lustful woman and the Machiavel with his tool-villain continue to be popular characters; and the tragic sense of Hieronimo and Hamlet that the world is a mass of public wrongs, an unweeded garden, leads to the inclusion of a good deal of satire on contemporary society.

In *The White Devil* and many of the other later plays derived from the revenge genre, the idea of revenge enters only near the middle of the play in response to earlier events. The revenger may be the antagonist, and then the revenge action will probably be subordinate to the willful action of the protagonist that brings it on. Kyd's influence may still be felt when we turn back from these later plays to note that he, too, introduces his main revenge action almost halfway through the play, although the play has been dominated by Revenge from the beginning. And Kyd has an antagonist "revenger," too, in Lorenzo.

It would of course be a gross exaggeration to contend that *The Spanish Tragedy* alone sets the pattern of later revenge plays. As I said in Chapter I, many works contributed to the tone, form, and content of Kyd's play, and many of these works also influenced the later writers directly. Moreover, there are sharp differences between Kyd's work and the later plays, especially in style. Tourneur, Webster, Middleton, and Ford are better poets than Kyd, partly for having heard and seen Shakespeare. A measure of the change in dramatic style that occurred between Kyd's writing of *The Spanish Tragedy* and Shakespeare's writing of *Hamlet* can be seen in the anonymous additions to Kyd's play that were written in about 1599–1601. The similarities that scholars have found between these passages and the work of Webster, Ben Jonson, Shakespeare, and Thomas Dekker may not have proved that one of these men was the author,[2] but collectively the similarities prove how typical the work is of dramatic writing at the end of the sixteenth century.

The main effect of each of the five additions is to build up the role of Hieronimo, heightening his motivation and the impact of his character by intensifying his grief-stricken madness and exploiting its pathos even more than Kyd had done. As a result, Kyd's plot and his characterization of Hieronimo are significantly altered in the revised play: Hieronimo suffers a spell of madness as early as the scene of his finding Horatio's body in Act II.v. He cannot accept his son's death and withdraws into the delusion that it is the body of some other person dressed in his clothes. This change introduces not only madness and the failure of Hieronimo's "eyes, no eyes" earlier than Kyd had done, but it especially emphasizes Hieronimo's isolation from the people around him, for Isabella and the servants Pedro and Jacques can all recognize Horatio perfectly well.

In Kyd's play we have already seen that man is tragically isolated, and in the additions the anonymous writer has concentrated our attention more and more on the lonely mind of Hieronimo in moments when, nearly oblivious of those around him, he is withdrawn into memories of his son and the murder. Thus in the very brief second addition in Act III.ii, all that is added of any importance is Hieronimo's offhand and bitterly ironical remark to Lorenzo about the murder of Horatio, a remark which destroys Kyd's image of the cautious and cunning Hieronimo in order to show that his obsession overcomes all else.

The bitterness and irony of Hieronimo's remark to Lorenzo, "The murder of a son, or so:/A thing of nothing, my lord," are developed fully in the third addition, at Act III.xi. 5. This speech is one of the greatest in the revised play for its exploitation of the pathos in the old man's ironies. Hieronimo tries to tell himself that the loss of a son is a small matter, but the ironic effect of his lines is to intensify his feelings and ours as he tells the moving story of the birth and growth of a child. He describes the child's helplessness and the youth's rebelliousness in terms so universal that some of what he says even sounds contemporary to a modern audience. Then, as if this has not been more than enough to move us, Hieronimo concludes by letting his newly intensified emotion break through the mask of irony, saying that Horatio was his entire hope, a far better son than the ordinary sort he has just described. No audience can fail to sympathize with the revenger's actions after this appeal.

The fourth addition, at the start of Act III.xiii, is a new version of Hieronimo's scene with Bazulto, the old man whose son has been murdered, whom the reviser has changed into a painter named Bazardo. It is night, and the servants Jacques and Pedro enter Hieronimo's arbor with torches to aid him in his mad quest to see better and so find Horatio again. As in Kyd's Act II.v., Hieronimo blames the darkness of night for Horatio's death, saying that lights like the servants' torches are futile and that the moon betrayed virtue by not shining to prevent Horatio's murder (III.xiii.27–50 in revised edition, and cf. Kyd's II.v.22–25). Isabella enters and draws Hieronimo's attention to the tree on which Horatio was hanged, and Hieronimo's curse on the tree looks forward to her mad suicide scene in Kyd's version.[3] The greater poetic power of the added speech of Hieronimo suggests one direction in which Elizabethan drama grew between 1590 and 1600:

[ISAB.] Down with these branches and these loathsome boughs
    Of this unfortunate and fatal pine:
    Down with them Isabella, rent them up
    And burn the roots from whence the rest is sprung:
    I will not leave a root, a stalk, a tree,
    A bough, a branch, a blossom, nor a leaf,
    No, not an herb within this garden plot—
    Accursed complot of my misery.
    Fruitless for ever may this garden be,
    Barren the earth . . . .
    And as I curse this tree from further fruit,
    So shall my womb be cursed for his sake,
    And with this weapon will I wound the breast,
                       She stabs herself.
    The hapless breast, that gave Horatio suck.
                  (Kyd's IV.ii.6–15, 35–38)
[HIER.] This was the tree, I set it of a kernel,
    And when our hot Spain could not let it grow,
    But that the infant and the human sap
    Began to wither, duly twice a morning
    Would I be sprinkling it with fountain water.
    At last it grew, and grew, and bore and bore,
    Till at the length
    It grew a gallows, and did bear our son.
    It bore thy fruit and mine: O wicked, wicked plant.
                (Additions, III.xiii.63–71)

Kyd's verse is rhetorically repetitious both between and within lines, and the relation between Isabella and the tree is more

allegorically pointed out than poetically created, though her
"*Barren* the earth" is a metaphorical gesture, however feeble.
In constrast, the passage in the addition of 1602 poetically fuses
the tree and its human fruit from infancy through their growth
into a gallows bearing a corpse.

But the scene with the Painter in the changed version is the
greatest piece of writing in the play, and its author knew it, for
the passage claims a superiority of dramatic poetry to painting
and proves its case through its expressive power. The claim is
made only ironically, for the Painter says he can render most of
the effects Hieronimo wants in a picture of Horatio's death and
Hieronimo's grief, but the poetic description Hieronimo gives
could never be duplicated anywhere, and he keeps pushing the
Painter beyond the limits of his art.

> [HIER.] . . . bring me forth in my shirt, and my gown under mine
>   arm, with my torch in my hand, and my sword reared up
>   thus: and with these words:
>   *What noise is this? who calls Hieronimo?*
>   May it be done?
> PAINT. Yea, sir.
> HIER. Well sir, then bring me forth, bring me through alley and
>   alley, still with a distracted countenance going along, and let
>   my hair heave up my night-cap. Let the clouds scowl, make
>   the moon dark, the stars extinct, the winds blowing, the bells
>   tolling, the owl shrieking, the toads croaking, the minutes jarr-
>   ing, and the clock striking twelve. And then at last, sir, start-
>   ing, behold a man hanging, and tottering and tottering, as you
>   know the wind will weave a man, and I with a trice to cut
>   him down. And looking upon him by the advantage of my
>   torch, find it to be my son Horatio. There you may show a
>   passion, there you may show a passion. Draw me like old
>   Priam of Troy, crying, "The house is a-fire, the house is a-fire,
>   as the torch over my head." Make me curse, make me rave,
>   make me cry, make me mad, make me well again, make me
>   curse hell, invocate heaven, and in the end, leave me in a
>   trance—and so forth.
> PAINT. And is this the end?
> HIER. O no, there is no end: the end is death and madness.
>   (III.xiii.139–63)

The commonplace Renaissance critical dictum, *"ut pictura poesis,"*
calls for the words of poetry to use images for *"expression*

through particulars of the essential significance of a subject" [4] in a way analogous to the use of images in the painting of the time. The author of the additions reverses this principle, in a sense, and dares a painter to render words and actions in oils. But the author's real purpose is to draw our attention to his own great art. In the concentrated power of its rendering of the scene that so well epitomizes the spirit of *The Spanish Tragedy*, the passage is a final microcosm in a play full of microcosms; and it is the tribute of a greater poet than Kyd to the old playwright's ability to inspire 'the essential tragic emotions of pity and fear.

Above all, the passage is eloquent proof of the hold Kyd's play had on the imaginations of Elizabethan audiences and writers, for it is a *retrospective* view that imparts to its subject all the magic we associate with the works that most impressed us in youth. The reviser and Hieronimo look back together, or rather the reviser looks back through Hieronimo's eyes, entering into his lonely terror to create the old scene anew.[5]

PAINT. And is this the end?
HIER. O no, there is no end: the end is death and madness.

The empty horror of these lines near the end of the scene with the Painter is fulfilled in the last of the additions, in which the reviser radically changes the speeches leading up to Hieronimo's death. In the new version Hieronimo is more than ever the master puppeteer in a mad fantasy of power over kings and even death. At the end, the reviser makes Hieronimo very self-consciously renounce speech, action, and life itself as a renunciation of a part in a play. His idea of himself as a puppeteer suddenly narrows to focus on his lonely self as puppet, with the continued delusion that no force governs him but his own will. He has succeeded in cutting all the cords of love and hate that related him to others, and now at last he can let his hand fall and rupture his part in the play by biting out his tongue and stabbing his heart. And his last action within his part is to applaud what he has acted: in a sense, his death projects him out of the play and into the audience, where he should most appropriately be seated with Revenge and the other puppet who has become "inward with revenge," Andrea. "O no, there is no end: the end is death and madness." The inexorable force of Nemesis sweeps a man to his doom, and the tragic writer shows man's greatness in his struggle to control his fate, his folly and his pathos in the delusion that he can ever succeed.

Notes and References

Preface and Chronology

1. For a variety of opinions on Kyd's authorship of disputed works, see Frederick S. Boas' introduction to his edition of *The Works of Thomas Kyd* (Oxford, 1901); K. Wiehl, "Thomas Kyd und die Autorschaft von *Soliman and Perseda, The First Part of Jeronimo* und *Arden of Feversham*," *Englische Studien*, XLIV (1912), 343–60; John J. Murray, "The Tragedye of Solyman and Perseda. Edited from the Original Text with Introduction and Notes," an unpublished New York University dissertation, *Dissertation Abstracts*, XX (1960), 3284; and Philip Edwards' introduction to the Revels Plays edition of *The Spanish Tragedy* (Cambridge, Mass., 1959). A comprehensive analysis of all questions of authorship is offered by Félix Carrère, *Le Théatre de Thomas Kyd* (Toulouse, 1951), pp. 229–306.

2. For a concise recent discussion of Kyd's life, see Edwards' introduction to *The Spanish Tragedy* in the Revels edition.

Chapter One

1. In Richard Brathwaite's *English Gentlewoman* (1631), quoted from Boas, p. xcvii. Boas has a good discussion of Kyd's reputation.

2. See Fredson T. Bowers, *Elizabethan Revenge Tragedy, 1587–1642* (Princeton, 1940), pp. 62–100. If Bowers is right that *Hamlet* was written before *The Spanish Tragedy*, then the Teutonic revenge tradition may be an important original source of Kydian tragedy.

3. For the relation of Seneca to Elizabethan tragedy, see John W. Cunliffe, *The Influence of Seneca on Elizabethan Tragedy* (New York, 1925); F.L. Lucas, *Seneca and Elizabethan Tragedy* (Cambridge, 1922); and T.S. Eliot's introduction to the reprint of the edition of Seneca prepared by Thomas Newton in 1581, *Seneca His Tenne Tragedies Translated into English* (London, 1927).

4. All references to the text of *The Spanish Tragedy* are to the edition prepared by Philip Edwards for the Revels Plays Series (Cambridge, Mass., 1959). Quoted passages are reprinted by permission of Harvard University Press and Methuen and Co.

5. For discussions of Kyd's *Cornelia* in relation to its French or-

iginal, see Alexander M. Witherspoon, *The Influence of Robert Garnier on Elizabethan Drama* ("Yale Studies in English," LXV [New Haven, 1924]); the introduction and notes to Boas' edition of Kyd; and Félix Carrère, *Le Théatre de Thomas Kyd.*

6. In "Intrigue in Elizabethan Tragedy," *Essays on Shakespeare and Elizabethan Drama in Honor of Hardin Craig,* ed. Richard Hosley (Columbia, Mo., 1962), pp. 37–44. See also Wolfgang Clemen, *English Tragedy Before Shakespeare: The Development of Dramatic Speech,* trans T.S. Dorsch (London, 1961), p. 112.

7. See Bernard Spivack, *Shakespeare and the Allegory of Evil* (New York, 1958), pp. 58 and 91.

8. Spivack, pp. 34, 360–61, notes that the character of Lorenzo is not "radically complicated" by the tradition of the Vice.

9. Clarence Valentine Boyer discusses the relation of Elizabethan ideas of Machiavelli to Seneca and to Lorenzo in *The Villain as Hero in Elizabethan Tragedy* (London, 1914), pp. 40–46, 99–103.

10. See Bowers, *Elizabethan Revenge Tragedy,* pp. 57–61.

11. For discussions of the adaptation of style to character and dramatic purpose, see Peter W. Biesterfeldt, *Die dramatische Technik Thomas Kyds* (Halle/Saale, 1936); Moody E. Prior, *The Language of Tragedy* (New York, 1947), pp. 49–57; and Clemen, *English Tragedy Before Shakespeare,* pp. 100–112.

12. Compare the similar analysis of Lorenzo and Bel-imperia in Boas, p. xxxiv, and in Michael H. Levin, " 'Vindicta Mihi!': Meaning, Morality, and Motivation in *The Spanish Tragedy,*" *Studies in English Literature,* IV (1964), 312–15.

13. Clemen, *English Tragedy Before Shakespeare,* p. 108.

14. Biesterfeldt, pp. 59–60. See Biesterfeldt's analysis for a valuable treatment of many of these matters, and compare the analysis of the plot structure by Ernest W. Talbert in *Elizabethan Drama and Shakespeare's Early Plays* (Chapel Hill, 1963), pp. 72–79.

15. For a full survey of act-structure in Renaissance theory and practice, see T.W. Baldwin, *Shakspere's Five-Act Structure* (Urbana, Ill., 1947).

16. Quoted from the translation by T.W. Baldwin, p. 112.

17. Some editors have started a new act after Act III.vii, on the supposition that one of Kyd's act-divisions with its chorus has been lost. For our present purpose, however, we need only see the structural logic of this supposition. See Philip Edwards' discussion of this question in his note to the beginning of Act III.viii, in his edition.

18. T. W. Baldwin, p. 222.

19. See Francis Fergusson, *The Idea of a Theater* (Princeton, 1949).

20. See William H. Wiatt, "The Dramatic Function of the Alex-

andro-Villuppo Episode in 'The Spanish Tragedy,' " *Notes and Queries,* N. S., V (1958), 327–29.

21. For general treatments of the importance of the play-within-the-play in Elizabethan drama, see Arthur Brown, "The Play within a Play: An Elizabethan Dramatic Device," *Essays and Studies,* XIII (1960), 36–48; Anne Righter, *Shakespeare and the Idea of the Play* (London, 1962); and Dieter Mehl "Forms and Functions of the Play within a Play," *Renaissance Drama,* VIII (1965), 41–61.

22. Cf. Clemen, p. 105.

23. Clemen, p. 101, notes that Kyd typically uses stichomythia next to long speeches for the sake of variety. See also Biesterfeldt, p. 73.

24. See especially Jonas A. Barish, "The Spanish Tragedy, *or The Pleasures and Perils of Rhetoric,*" *Elizabethan Theatre,* Stratford-Upon-Avon Studies, ed. John Russell Brown and Bernard Harris, IX (1966), 59–85.

Chapter Two

1. See Wiatt, cited in n. 20, chap. i.

2. Biesterfeldt, p. 72; Clemen, p. 104.

3. Compare the rather different discussions of tragic theme and effect by Biesterfeldt, pp. 50–53; Carrère, pp. 67–73; Harbage; and Levin—already cited—and by T.B. Tomlinson, *A Study of Elizabethan and Jacobean Tragedy* (Cambridge, 1964), pp. 73–84; and Kurt Wittig, "Gedanken zu Kyd's *Spanish Tragedie,*" in *Strena Anglica,* ed. Gerhard Dietrich and Fritz W. Schulze (Halle/Saale, 1956), pp. 133–77. The interpretations by Philip Edwards in *Thomas Kyd and Early Elizabethan Tragedy* (London, 1966), and G.K. Hunter, "*Ironies of Justice in* The Spanish Tragedy," *Renaissance Drama,* VIII (1965), 89–104, came to hand after the completion of my study, but I am pleased to find that we are in substantial agreement on some of the implications of the play's structure.

4. This thematic question is considered in detail by Bowers in *Elizabethan Revenge Tragedy,* pp. 65–82, by Edwards in his introduction to the Revels edition of the play, and by Levin. See also John D. Ratliff, "Hieronimo Explains Himself," *Studies in Philology,* LIV (1957), 112–18; Ernst de Chickera, "Divine Justice and Private Revenge in 'The Spanish Tragedy,' " *Modern Language Review,* LVII (1962), 228–32; S.F. Johnson, "*The Spanish Tragedy,* or Babylon Revisited," in *Essays on Shakespeare and Elizabethan Drama,* ed. Richard Hosley (Columbia, Mo., 1962), pp. 23–36; and Ejner J. Jensen, "Kyd's *Spanish Tragedy:* The Play Explains Itself," *Journal of English and Germanic Philology,* LXIV (1965), 7–16.

5. "Envy" meant "malice," but it also carried the meaning of malicious desire for what another person possesses.

6. S.F. Johnson, "*The Spanish Tragedy*, or Babylon Revisited," pp. 24–27.

7. Again see Biesterfeldt, p. 72; Clemen, p. 104.

8. Cf. The Discussion of Shakespeare's similar view in John Lawlor, *The Tragic Sense in Shakespeare* (London, 1960), especially pp. 153–183.

Chapter Three

1. Cf. Biesterfeldt, pp. 53–55.

2. See Howard Baker, *Induction to Tragedy* (University, La., 1939), pp. 98–118; Prior, *The Language of Tragedy*, p. 49.

Chapter Four

1. Clemen, p. 102.

2. Prior, pp. 50–51.

Chapter Five

1. Talbert suggests that Kyd may have intended the two letters of Bel-imperia and Pedringano as a structural frame for his "emphasis on Lorenzo's concatenated plots," *Elizabethan Drama and Shakespeare's Early Plays*, p. 73.

Chapter Six

1. See especially Ratliff, "Hieronimo Explains Himself"; Bowers, "A Note on *The Spanish Tragedy*," *Modern Language Notes*, LIII (1938), 590–91; William Empson, "The Spanish Tragedy," *Nimbus*, III (Summer, 1956), 16–29, reprinted in *Elizabethan Drama: Modern Essays in Criticism*, ed. Ralph J. Kaufmann (New York, 1961), pp. 60–80; and David Laird, "Hieronimo's Dilemma," *Studies in Philology*, LXII (1965), 137–46.

Chapter Seven

1. Charles K. Cannon, "The Relation of the Additions of *The Spanish Tragedy* to the Original Play," *Studies in English Literature*, II (1962), 229–39; cf. the interpretation of the garden by Johnson, p. 26.

2. See Edwards' introduction to his edition, pp. xxxiv–xl; Levin L. Schücking, *Die Zusätze zur "Spanish Tragedy,"* Berichte über die Verhandlungen der Sächsischen Akademie der Wissenschaften zu Leipzig, Band 90, Heft 2 (Leipzig, 1938); and Kurt Wittig, "Gedanken zu Kyd's *Spanish Tragedie.*"

3. See Charles Cannon's essay and Chapter VIII below for evidence that the reviser knew Kyd's play well.

Chapter Eight

1. Especially see Bowers' *Elizabethan Revenge Tragedy*.

2. See Edwards' introduction to his edition, pp. lxi–lxvi.

3. On this and other points of interpretation, compare Cannon's essay on "The Relation of the Additions of *The Spanish Tragedy* to the Original Play."

4. Rosemond Tuve, *Elizabethan and Metaphysical Imagery* (Chicago, 1947), p. 52.

5. If this were a more conventional passage, one could be satisfied merely to say that it is a conventional Senecan retrospective narrative. See the discussion of the convention by Clemen, p. 24.

Selected Bibliography

BOAS, FREDERICK S. (ed.). *The Works of Thomas Kyd.* Oxford: The Clarendon Press, 1901. Introduction, now out of date, surveys questions of Kyd's life, works, and influence.

EDWARDS, PHILIP (ed.). *The Spanish Tragedy.* Cambridge, Mass.: Harvard University Press, 1959. Now the standard text for the study of Kyd's play and its context.

BARISH, JONAS A. "The Spanish Tragedy, *or The Pleasures and Perils of Rhetoric*," *Elizabethan Theatre,* Stratford-Upon-Avon Studies, ed. JOHN RUSSELL BROWN and BERNARD HARRIS, IX (1966), 59–85. Shows how Kyd uses the figures of rhetoric to articulate and give form to dramatic action and theme. In the later part of the play sees a disjunction of "thought and word, word and deed."

BIESTERFELDT, PETER W. *Die dramatische Technik Thomas Kyds.* Halle/Saale: Max Niemeyer, 1936. Detailed analysis of theme, plot, and character in *The Spanish Tragedy.*

BOWERS, FREDSON T. *Elizabethan Revenge Tragedy, 1587–1642.* Princeton: Princeton University Press, 1940. Full study of genre.

———. "A Note on *The Spanish Tragedy*," *Modern Language Notes,* LIII (1938), 590–91. Shows that "*Vindicta Mihi*" is biblical; we must see that Hieronimo turns away from Christian teaching here.

BOYER, CLARENCE V. *The Villain as Hero in Elizabethan Tragedy.* London: Routledge, 1914. Argues that Lorenzo is a villainous revenger but Hieronimo is justified by a code of revenge.

CANNON, CHARLES K. "The Relation of the Additions of *The Spanish Tragedy* to the Original Play," *Studies in English Literature,* II (1962), 229–39. The additions develop the universal and eternal implications of the action.

CARRÈRE, FÉLIX. *Le Théâtre de Thomas Kyd.* Toulouse: Édouard Privat, 1951. A study of scholarly and critical problems, from Kyd's life and the authorship of disputed plays to the interpretation of *The Spanish Tragedy.*

CHICKERA, ERNST DE. "Divine Justice and Private Revenge in 'The Spanish Tragedy,'" *Modern Language Review*, LVII (1962), 228–32. Argues that Hieronimo seeks divine justice but that when he is forced to do evil to repay evil he becomes a tragic victim of the truth that they who use the sword must perish by it.

CLEMEN, WOLFGANG. *English Tragedy Before Shakespeare: The Development of Dramatic Speech*, trans. T.S. DORSCH. London: Methuen, 1961. A study of the rhetorical conventions and their use and modification by Kyd and other writers.

EDWARDS, PHILIP. *Thomas Kyd and Early Elizabethan Tragedy.* ("Writers and Their Work," No. 192.) London: Longmans, Green, 1966. Two most important points in this long essay are that Kyd shows men acting blindly, not knowing they are "puppets . . . controlled by superior forces," and that since Kyd uses a "neutral pagan metaphor for the government of the universe," we should not concern ourselves with a specifically Christian judgment in evaluating Hieronimo's tragedy.

EMPSON, WILLIAM. "The Spanish Tragedy," *Nimbus*, III (Summer, 1956), pp. 16–29, reprinted in *Elizabethan Drama: Modern Essays in Criticism*, ed. RALPH J. KAUFMANN. New York: Oxford University Press, 1961. Contends that Hieronimo is mad or at least tragically confused in the "*Vindicta mihi*" soliloquy.

HARBAGE, ALFRED. "Intrigue in Elizabethan Tragedy," in *Essays on Shakespeare and Elizabethan Drama in Honor of Hardin Craig*, ed. RICHARD HOSLEY. Columbia, Mo.: University of Missouri Press, 1962. Suggests that "Perhaps Kyd's greatest innovation was to employ comic methods with tragic materials, thus creating a species of comitragedy."

HUNTER, G. K. "*Ironies of Justice in* The Spanish Tragedy," *Renaissance Drama*, VIII (1965), 89–104. Argues that a working out of divine justice through the action controlled by Revenge is the "thematic center" of the play. Argues that the structure implies a series of levels of awareness, "an ironic mode of construction for the play."

JENSEN, EJNER J. "Kyd's *Spanish Tragedy*: The Play Explains Itself," *Journal of English and Germanic Philology*, LXIV (1965), 7–16. Argues that the main theme is justice, and that Kyd justifies Hieronimo by giving him the backing of divine powers and by showing that he is forced to act as he does.

JOHNSON, S. F. "*The Spanish Tragedy*, or Babylon Revisited," in *Essays on Shakespeare and Elizabethan Drama in Honor of Hardin Craig*, ed. RICHARD HOSLEY. Columbia, Mo.: University of Missouri Press, 1962. Studies in detail the relations of the biblical story of the fall of Babylon to Kyd's play; argues that

Hieronimo's revenge is basically an act of justice in accord with the Mosaic code.

LAIRD, DAVID. "Hieronimo's Dilemma," *Studies in Philology,* LXII (1965), 137–46. Contends that Hieronimo's "Vindicta mihi" soliloquy is a "careful, clear-headed deliberation" in which all moral issues are dealt with logically.

LEVIN, MICHAEL HENRY. " 'Vindicta mihi!': Meaning, Morality, and Motivation in *The Spanish Tragedy,*" *Studies in English Literature,* IV (1964), 307–24. Says that we are to see the guilt of Hieronimo, yet must sympathize with him. "He may be absolved in heaven, but he must die on earth . . . because murder, whatever its motivation, is a fatal violation of . . . a higher law."

PRIOR, MOODY E. *The Language of Tragedy.* New York: Columbia University Press, 1947. A study of the language of tragedy in relation to action, character, and theme.

RATLIFF, JOHN D. "Hieronimo Explains Himself," *Studies in Philology,* LIV (1957), 112–18. Argues that in its context Hieronimo's *"Vindicta Mihi"* soliloquy justifies his course of action in revenge.

SCHÜCKING, LEVIN L. *Die Zusätze zur "Spanish Tragedy."* Berichte über die Verhandlungen der Sächsischen Akademie der Wissenschaften zu Leipzig. Band 90, Heft 2. Leipzig: S. Hirzel, 1938. Says that even the earliest text of the play has been revised and contains both original and revised passages, and that most of the additions of 1602 were intended to replace passages that have nevertheless not been deleted.

TALBERT, ERNEST W. *Elizabethan Drama and Shakespeare's Early Plays.* Chapel Hill: University of North Carolina Press, 1963. Includes an analysis of *The Spanish Tragedy* showing how Kyd made use of the conventions of contemporary and earlier drama.

TOMLINSON, T. B. *A Study of Elizabethan and Jacobean Tragedy.* Cambridge: Cambridge University Press, 1964. Contains a critical discussion of language, character, structure, and theme in *The Spanish Tragedy.*

WIATT, WILLIAM H. "The Dramatic Function of the Alexandro-Villuppo Episode in 'The Spanish Tragedy,' " *Notes and Queries,* N.S. 5 (1958), 327–29. Argues that because we see the Viceroy act wrongly on the basis of false information, we sympathize with Hieronimo in the next scene when he delays action in order to confirm information he is given.

WITTIG, KURT. "Gedanken zu Kyd's *Spanish Tragedie,*" in *Strena Anglica,* ed. Gerhard Dietrich and Fritz W. Schulze. Halle/Saale: Max Niemeyer, 1956. Like Schücking, Wittig thinks the play has been revised more than once.

Index

Aeschylus, 11

Beaumont, Francis, 153, 154; *The Maid's Tragedy,* 154
Bible, 81
Brathwaite, Richard, 11

Chettle, Henry, 153
Classical literature, influence of on Kyd, 11ff

Dekker, Thomas, 155
Donatus, Aelius, 19–23

Euripedes, 11

Fletcher, John, 153; *The Maid's Tragedy,* 154
Ford, John, 11, 153, 154, 155

Garnier, Robert, 5

Heywood, Thomas, 5
Horace, *Ars Poetica,* 19

Interludes, influenced Kyd, 11

Jonson, Ben, 155

Kyd, Thomas

WORKS ATTRIBUTED TO:

Arden of Feversham, 5
The First Part of Jeronimo, 5
the lost *Hamlet,* 5, 11
King Leir, 5
The Murder of John Brewen, 5

The Rare Triumphs of Love and Fortune, 5
Titus Andronicus, 5
The Tragedy of Soliman and Perseda, 5
The Troublesome Reign of King John, 5

WRITINGS OF:

Cornelia, a translation, 5, 12–13
The Householder's Philosophy, a translation, 5
The Spanish Tragedy:
Characterization in, 15ff
Influences on, 11ff
Interpretation of, 22ff
Language of, 12, 16–17, 19, 24–26, 32–33, 36, 52–53, 61–63, 66, 78, 81–85, 86–90, 92–96, 100–102, 120, 121–22
Plot construction in, 19ff, 55–58, 76–78, 97, 118, 135, 138
Scene construction in, 24–26
Staging of, 14–15, 142–48

Landino, Christopher, 19–23

Machiavelli, Niccolo, 14, 81, 104–5
Marlowe, Christopher, 153; *Doctor Faustus,* 81
Marston, John, 11, 153
Medici family, influence of novelle about, 14
Middleton, Thomas, 11, 153, 155; *The Changeling,* 154; *Women Beware Women,* 154
Morality play, influence of, 11, 13–14, 68, 81

74362

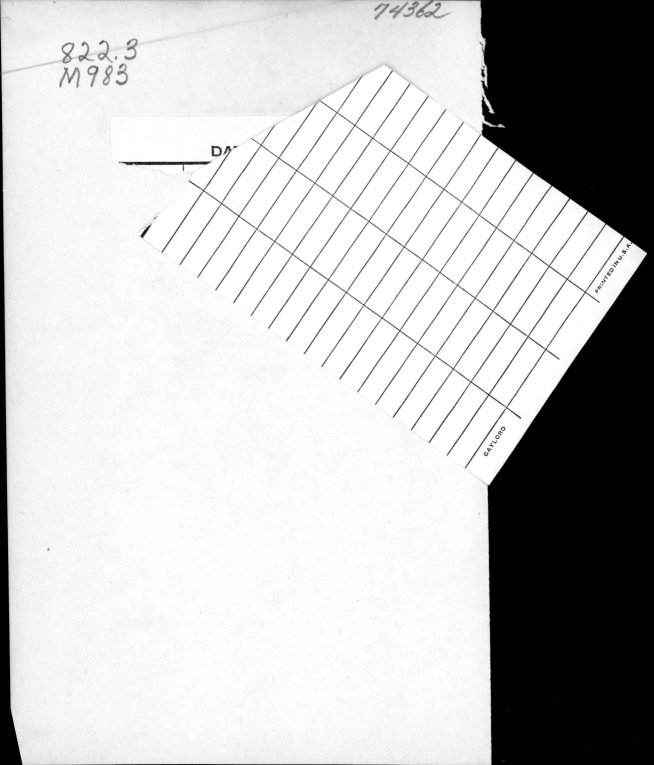

*THE MAGIC
MOTH*

THE MAGIC
MOTH

by Virginia Lee
Drawings by Richard Cuffari

Houghton Mifflin/Clarion Books/New York

Houghton Mifflin/Clarion Books
52 Vanderbilt Avenue, New York, NY 10017

Text copyright © 1972 by Virginia L. Ewbank
Drawings copyright © 1972 by Houghton Mifflin/Clarion Books

ISBN: 0-395-28863-0
Paperback ISBN: 0-395-30008-8
(Previously published by The Seabury Press under ISBN: 0-8164-3043-8)

Library of Congress Catalog Card Number: 73-171862

Design by Judith Lerner
Printed in the United States of America

Fourth Printing

for Lori Ann and my father

CHAPTER ONE

Iᴅ, sᴏᴍᴇ evening around 5:30, you were to take a walk down 128th Street, you would come to a gray house with "1205" over the front door. The grass in the small front yard is cut, but the edges are not trimmed. The paint is peeling, but not as badly as on some of the other houses on the street. This is an older neighborhood, and most of the people who live here cannot afford new paint for their houses as often as they need it.

If you looked through a window on the south side of

1205, you would see the George Foss family eating dinner around a brown, varnished, picnic-style table. George sits at one end in his comfortable old armchair. Irene, his wife, sits at the other end in a dining room chair with two red pillows on the seat and back.

On the bench at George's left is six-year-old Mark-O (for Mark Oliver) where Father can catch his milk when he spills it. Julie, nine, sits on her father's right by the kitchen door, so she can run for the sponge if Father misses.

Stephen, fifteen, sits next to Julie, but fairly near the middle of the table, where he can reach all the food. Barbie, fourteen, sits across from Stephen because that is the only place left.

Julie hates sitting where she does, because both Father's and Stephen's feet are big and she is always

getting tangled up with them under the table. It makes Stephen mad, and Father says, "Both of you keep your feet where they belong!" But no one ever says that to Father. Oh, no!

One evening the family was sitting as usual around the dinner table. It was the 27th of February, and they had just finished singing "Happy Birthday" to Augustus, the third guinea pig.

The Foss family has an interesting tradition, which did not come from anywhere. They started it themselves. They celebrate every birthday of every animal in the household just as they do their own. Since there are two dogs, an unknown number of cats who come and go, and four guinea pigs, there are several birthday cakes for dinner every month.

Frequently they get mixed up on the guinea pigs, and they have to make up the cats' birth dates, so it is likely that many of the animals get celebrated two or three times a year.

Whenever Mother is ready to bake a cake, she asks, "Whose cake is it to be this time?" If someone can remember an animal who has not had a birthday recently, there are candles on the cake that night.

The Fosses were starting on Augustus' chocolate marble cake with peppermint ice cream when Julie asked, "Hey! Whose birthday's next?"

"Maryanne's," Mother replied, putting a spoonful of the pink ice cream in a small dish.

"When is it?" asked Mark-O of anybody.

"Ninth of March," answered Stephen with his mouth full.

Mother got up from the table and took the dish of ice cream into Maryanne's room, just off the dining room. It has been over a year now since Maryanne, who is ten, last ate at the table with the family, or saw the tutor from school, or even got up out of bed. She has a heart defect.

Barbie, Julie, and Stephen take turns with Mother helping Maryanne eat her meals. They bring her little tidbits of the tenderest parts of the roast, or carefully buttered peas, or a bit of mashed potato dripping in gravy, and hold the plate while Maryanne takes a few bites. When she gets tired, they feed her the last of her food.

They also take turns thinking up special ways to decorate her portions of the meal. Sometimes Mark-O picks a little sprig of parsley for the potatoes (it grows wild under the kitchen window). Or Julie crumbles over a vegetable a piece of crisp bacon that she's saved from breakfast.

"I hope Maryanne wants green cake with peanut frosting for her birthday," screeched Mark-O after Mother had left the dining room.

Barbie looked at him severely. "Stop it, Mark-O. You know Maryanne can't eat cake. Momma will choose the cake, and you will like it or lump it."

Lately Barbie was acting more and more like a mother instead of a sister, and both Mark-O and Julie wished she'd change back. Mark-O decided to ignore her and turned to Father.

"Daddy, why can't Maryanne eat cake anymore? When can she?"

"Well," said Father slowly, "you know how sick she has been. That's why." He paused. "Perhaps she won't be able to eat cake, ever. Maybe she will have to go away soon."

"Where is she going?" asked Julie. "To the hospital again?"

Maryanne had been in the hospital for a long while when she was small, but when she came home she was not much better. Then, last year, a famous surgeon had operated on her heart. But afterward he had explained to Mr. and Mrs. Foss that there were some things doctors could not yet repair, and this was one of them.

"No—she won't be going to the hospital this time," said Father.

"I know what Daddy means," said Barbie. "He means Maryanne is going to die."

Everyone stopped eating. They were silent. You could

hear the hum of the electric clock on the wall.

Then Julie started to cry, and she put her napkin over her face.

Mother came out of the bedroom. She looked at Julie, then at the quietness of the others. Then she looked at Father. "Did you tell them?" she asked.

"Yes," he nodded. He took the big storybook with the green cover from the bookcase and went into Maryanne's room.

CHAPTER TWO

M ARK-O got down on his hands and knees and crawled into the bedroom after Father. He thought that if he pretended he was a cat no one would notice. No one did. He wanted to look at Maryanne when she didn't know he was looking. He wanted to see if she really looked like someone who was going to die.

William Guinea Pig had died last summer, and Mark-O had cried, and they had buried it and got Mark-O a new one. It looked exactly like the one that died. But when

Mark-O looked at Maryanne, he thought, "I don't see how we could find another Maryanne." He felt terrible.

Father was reading about a princess named Proserpine, who was stolen away by a wicked king in a cave deep under the ground. The whole world was so sad that the trees lost their leaves and the grass dried up, and snow lay all over the earth. Later, Proserpine got to come back for half a year, and the green things grew again.

"And that," finished Father, "is why we have spring and summer and fall and winter."

For some reason, the story made Mark-O feel better. Maybe if Maryanne died and went away, she would come back. He went out to the living room to find Julie. Julie was his favorite relative. She didn't mind noise, she liked throwing things around and making messes, and she was always cheerful.

Mother was on the phone in the study, and Barbie was stacking dirty dishes.

"Barbie, where's Julie?"

"She's in the bathroom. She locked herself in and won't come out."

Mark-O went over to the door.

"Hey—leave her alone!" Barbie said. "She'll come out when she wants to."

Mark-O stomped up to his own room, which he shared with Stephen. The lights were out and there were just the lights from the hall. Stephen was sitting on the edge of his bed, his chin in his hands. He was thinking about Maryanne and how she always listened to him tell about football practice, even though she didn't know how to play.

There was a crayon line down the middle of the room, which Stephen had drawn three weeks ago.

"Mark-O," Stephen had said, "your side is over there, and mine is over here. If you get one toy on my side, I will disappear it! There's a secret hole under my bed. I'll drop the toy down it, and it will go clear through to China."

Mark-O tried to be careful, but one day two weeks ago his best orange ball had gotten over the line and disappeared. When he told Mother what Stephen had done with the ball, Mother had just smiled and said she was sure it would turn up.

Now, as Mark-O stood in the doorway looking at the line, he saw his orange ball, lying exactly within it on his side.

"My ball! Stevie, you got it back. How did you get it?" Mark-O cried.

"Well, I'll tell you, Mark-O, that ball was such a good ball that when I dropped it down the hole it bounced back up. It was so far to China that it took a whole week to go down and a whole week to bounce back." Stephen

16

was smiling in an odd way.

"It did?" Mark-O's eyes were big. He could hardly believe such an amazing thing.

"Stevie, Maryanne will come back too, won't she?"

Stephen's smile disappeared and he didn't answer right away. When he did his voice sounded crackly as it often did lately. Father said it was because he was growing up.

"Well, no, she won't. But where she is going it will be nice."

"Is she going to China?"

"Creepers! Don't you know anything? Of course she's not going to China. When people die they go to heaven."

"Is heaven under the ground?"

"Of course not. Quit asking questions."

Mark-O took his ball and went back down to the kitchen. Mother was washing dishes and Barbie was drying. "Momma, can I give Maryanne a present for the guinea pig's birthday?"

"Of course, if you want to."

"What are you going to give her?" Barbie asked.

"My China ball," Mark-O answered, running off.

"Your what?" she asked, but he was already gone.

He ran into Maryanne's room. Father was giving her a drink of water, and she was sitting up part way on her pillows.

"Maryanne, guess what? Today was Augustus' birthday, and I got a present for you. Want it?"

Maryanne was sleepy, but she smiled and nodded. She liked Mark-O's presents. Nearly every day he brought her a bug in a jar or a pretty rock from the driveway or a drawing of something he saw going by on the street in front of the living room windows.

Last fall he had brought her a brilliant red and green caterpillar which had woven a cocoon. The jar stayed by her bed, and every day she expected to see a butterfly come out. Lately she had left the lid off so that the butterfly could get out when it was ready.

Before Maryanne had to stay in bed, she would often sit on the porch or on a blanket in the back yard, looking

at small things near her. She made up stories about them for Mark-O, who loved stories even when they had no ending or middle, and Maryanne's stories often had only a beginning.

After Mark-O began bringing presents to her, she still made up stories about them, but in the last few weeks she would only say, "I'm too tired," when he asked for one.

Now she held out her hands for the present and Mark-O put the ball in them. "It's pretty orange," she said. "That's your best ball. I thought Stephen put it down his China hole."

"He got it back. Guess what? It was such a good ball, it bounced back—all the way from China. It took one week to go and one week to come back. All the way under the ground. It's really special now."

Maryanne looked at it and rolled it around between her fingers. "It even feels different. I wish I could go all the way to China and come back, and I wouldn't be sick anymore." She closed her eyes.

"What do . . . ?" Mark-O started to ask, but Father shushed him.

"That was a very nice present, Mark-O," he said. "You were generous to give Maryanne your best ball. Maybe she can put it under her pillow and have a dream about it. Kiss her good night now. It's bedtime."

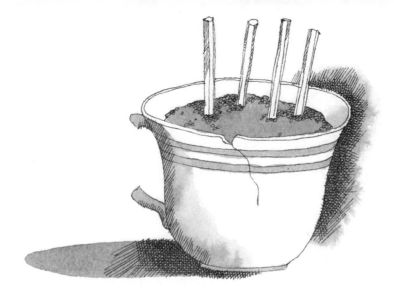

CHAPTER THREE

Next morning there were fresh grapefruit for breakfast, and new sharp metal spoons to eat them with.

"I got them with a tea coupon, and the grapefruit were ten for a dollar at the sale yesterday," Barbie announced. She was learning how to plan food-buying in her ninth grade home economics class, and had been doing much of the grocery shopping since Maryanne got so sick.

"The spoons are so Momma doesn't have to cut all the sections for us," Barbie said. "Look, you do it like this."

She showed everybody how to use the spoons, but it was hard the first time and before long there was juice all over everything. Mark-O's mess was the worst, but nobody criticized him. Father just said, "You'll get the hang of it after a while."

While Mark-O was working with his grapefruit, he found something. "Look, Barbie, it's a funny seed."

"It's awful big, all right," said Barbie. "My seeds are big, too."

"But look, its got a tail on it."

"Oh." Barbie stopped eating and looked closer. "Mark-O, that's a plant coming out of it! See the little leaves starting at the end?"

"Plant it, Mark-O," Julie urged. "It will grow a grapefruit tree."

"Momma, can I plant it?"

"Yes. After breakfast. Eat now. Your eggs are getting cold."

After breakfast, Barbie grabbed her lunch and ran for her jacket and books.

"Brush your teeth!" called Father.

"I can't, I'm going to miss my bus," called Barbie as she slammed the door.

"Darn!" exclaimed Julie. "She's always copping out on the breakfast dishes!" Julie's bus came an hour later than Barbie's and she was expected to clear the table and stack the dishes, but Barbie was *supposed* to help. When she couldn't, Mark-O got tagged for the job.

Mark-O ran for the bathroom. It was the safest place to be when it was time to clear the table. He locked the door. He'd show Julie she wasn't the only one who could hole up in there when people wanted her.

When he couldn't hear dishes clattering any longer, he flushed the toilet and made a noise with the water faucet, which rumbled when you turned it on a certain way. Sauntering out to the kitchen, he asked Mother, "Can we plant the seed, now?"

"Right now," she said, putting the last bowl in the dish drainer.

Just then, Stephen rushed through the kitchen, grabbed his lunch, whooshed through the door and slammed it behind him. Shortly after, Julie walked slowly in. She looked at the clock, grabbed her jacket and yelled, "I didn't know it was that late!" and slammed the door behind her.

Mark-O felt confused. Whenever he started something ten different things happened all at once, and he never got to finish.

"Boy, I'm glad they're all gone!" he sighed.

"Yes, I suppose you must be," answered Mother. "Now, take this old cup outside and fill it with dirt."

Mark-O went out on the front porch, slamming the

door like the others. He scooped up a cupful of dirt from the flower bed by the porch. Underneath the azalea bush he could see the little stick with the paper on it that said, "William Guinea Pig." The dirt was cold and wet and heavy. "That's an awful place for William to be," Mark-O said to himself as he went back inside.

"Momma, do you think William is cold out there?"

"No, I don't," she answered.

"Why?"

"Well, because after guinea pigs die, they don't feel anything anymore."

"Are you sure?"

"I am very sure."

"Is that what will happen to Maryanne?"

"Yes," said Mother slowly, "but that is only part of what will happen. That is the least important part."

"What else will happen?"

Mother sighed. "Did you ever go to sleep and dream you were someplace else?"

"I did once when I dreamed I was in an airplane flying over the ocean."

"I remember that night, too. You kicked your covers off and got cold. I came in and covered you up. Do you remember that?"

"No."

"Did you know that you were in your bed and that you were cold?"

"No. I really thought I was in the airplane."

"That's a little bit like what will happen to Maryanne. She will go to sleep and not know she is here. The important part of her, that does the dreaming, will be someplace else."

"Oh." Mark-O felt better.

"Let's put your seed in the dirt now," said Mother. "In fact, let's put three or four of these seeds in, and stick a match by each one to mark it. We'll see which one comes up first."

Mark-O punched a hole for each seed with the match, and dropped in the seed. Then he lit four matches over the sink and blew them out. He put a match beside each seed and pressed down the dirt.

Mark-O picked up the cup and went into Maryanne's room. She was lying very still. Her eyes were almost closed, but she was not asleep because when she heard him she opened her eyes and turned her head.

"I'm glad you're not asleep," Mark-O said. "Look, I planted four grapefruit seeds, and I'm having a contest to see which one comes up first."

Maryanne was silent for a while, then she said very softly, "What will you give the seed that comes up first?"

Mark-O was puzzled. He hadn't thought of that. "I know, I'll give the seed to you."

"Okay," Maryanne said, and closed her eyes.

Mark-O huffed. "Why do you always have to go to sleep when I'm talking to you?" When Maryanne didn't stir, he ran back to the kitchen.

"Momma! I think Maryanne went to sleep! Is she all right?"

Mother seemed a little upset. "Look, Mark-O, don't worry if Maryanne goes to sleep. It's good for her. And please don't talk to Maryanne about it."

"Don't you want her to know?"

"She already knows, but I don't want her to worry about going to sleep." She put her hands on his shoulders. "Mark-O, this is a very hard time for all of us. We will talk about it some more later, all right?"

Mother looked tired. What is more, she said, "I'm tired. You go get ready for school now."

Mark-O's kindergarten class was in the morning and he got home for lunch every day. He put the cup with the grapefruit seeds in it on the kitchen windowsill and ran to get his jacket.

CHAPTER FOUR

ALL THAT WEEK, things went on as they always had. Julie was almost late for her bus every morning, and Barbie missed hers once and had to walk. Every night they argued over who cleared the table. Every morning, Mark-O fed the guinea pigs and looked to see if the seeds had come up, and every night he asked Stephen a million questions about China and other things that were on his mind. The seeds never came up, and he was never satisfied with Stephen's answers. Most of the time Stephen would say, "I dunno. I guess you better ask Dad."

Sometimes, Mark-O thought, big brothers are the stupidest people in the world. When he said so to Father, Father just smiled and remarked, "Perhaps the feeling is mutual."

In between times, Mark-O took his endless stream of worms and leaves and empty pill bottles and loose glass beads that had rolled under the furniture in to Maryanne. He was increasingly disappointed because she was asleep so much, and when she was awake, she didn't say much to him.

"What's the matter?" he asked one afternoon when she did not smile at one of his presents. "Don't you feel good?"

"No." Maryanne closed her eyes tight and would not say anything more.

Mark-O went to find Mother. "Momma, Maryanne doesn't feel so good. You better give her a pill."

"I can't do that just now," she said. "I already did give her one." Then she went into Maryanne's room and shut the door.

Mark-O knew that when Mother did that he was absolutely not to go in after her. He didn't like being shut out. What was going on in there? His stomach began to hurt. Finally, he went to look at his seeds for the second time that day. Still, nothing. Angrily he dug down with his finger and found one of the seeds. He put it in the palm of his hand. The seed was nearly black, and it crumbled into several pieces. It seemed to be all dried up.

Just then, Barbie came in from school and saw him. "What did you do that for?" she asked. "If you dig your seeds up they won't grow."

"They won't anyway. Look at this—it's all ruined! It's dead!"

"No, it's not. All the seeds look that way right now. No! Don't dig them all up!"

Mark-O stopped just before he had emptied the whole cup out on the counter. "How do you know they are all that way?"

"Because I've grown more seeds than you ever will, and dug up lots of them when I was little. They all looked that way. You want plants, you take my word for it."

"But why?"

"I don't know. But the outsides of the seeds have to dry up and fall apart so the plants inside can grow."

"Is that what happens to all seeds?"

"It is if you plant them."

Mark-O put back the cup on the windowsill and went out on the porch. He sat down to wait for Julie. Presently she came running up the walk from the bus stop, all out of breath. That was the way she went everywhere—in a rush.

"What are you doing, Mark-O?" she asked cheerfully. "You look awful serious."

"I'm thinking."

"You? What are you thinking about?"

"I'm thinking I'd like to dig up William and see if he was going to grow into a plant. But I don't dare because if I did and he were, he wouldn't anyway."

Julie rolled her eyes and made a long face. "Goodness, Mark-O, you wouldn't want to do a thing like that. There wouldn't be much of anything left and besides it would look awful and besides that he won't make a plant anyway. Let's go have a snack."

"Why wouldn't there be anything left?"

"Because, if you bury something it just becomes part of the ground after a while."

Mark-O's stomach still hurt and he didn't want a snack. He started to stomp upstairs, but Barbie came out of the study and said in a fierce whisper, "You keep quiet! Maryanne's *very* sick. I have just called the doctor for Mother, and you are to *be quiet.*"

Mark-O looked at her and thought, "You don't have to be so cross." Out loud, he said, "You aren't my boss." But anyway he tiptoed over to the davenport and sat down.

"I'm sorry, Mark-O," said Barbie. "I didn't mean to jump on you, but really, you don't have to stomp all the time. It's just as easy to walk."

"What's going on in Maryanne's room?" he asked.

"I don't know," Barbie answered.

Why is it that all the important things happen under the ground or behind closed doors? Mark-O wondered.

Julie was sitting on the dining room bench and he could just see her through the door. She wasn't eating her snack. Barbie sat in the easy chair and said nothing. She was frowning and biting on a nail.

After a long while, the doorbell rang.

"I thought doctors didn't come to houses," Julie said. "Before, we always took Maryanne."

"This is special," answered Barbie as she went to the door. She opened it for a man in a black overcoat, carrying a bag.

"This is the room, over here," she said, taking his coat and pointing to the door.

The man stopped and looked at Mark-O and Julie and asked them their names. "I'm Doctor Turner," he said. "I'll come back out and talk to you in a few minutes." Then he entered the bedroom, closing the door behind him.

In a few minutes he came out again, and Mother followed. Julie and Barbie had joined Mark-O on the davenport, and Dr. Turner sat down with them.

"Maryanne won't be with us much longer," he said. "Perhaps she will leave today." He said it in such a normal tone of voice that he might have been talking about Maryanne going on an ordinary trip.

"Why don't you take her to the hospital and make her well?" Julie asked. She almost sounded angry.

"Well," the doctor answered, "we have tried everything, including surgery, which you are old enough to remember. There is nothing else that *can* be done. Maryanne has been growing bigger all the time, and her heart is not strong enough to keep pumping for her as it did when she was small. And she is happiest in her own home, don't you think?"

"Ye-e-s," answered Julie.

"Can I go see her?" asked Mark-O.

"Yes, go ahead."

The doctor turned to Mother and said, "The medication I gave her should last for quite a while. She probably won't need any more. If you want me, just call. I'm off duty the rest of the day."

He left and Barbie and Mark-O and Julie all three went into Maryanne's room. They stood and looked at her, but all three felt too strange to say a word. Maryanne seemed to be asleep but they could hear her breathing in short, sharp breaths. Just then, she opened her eyes and smiled at Mark-O.

"Do you feel better, now?" he asked.

Maryanne nodded sleepily.

Mother said, "The doctor gave her something better than a pill. Now she feels much better."

So did Mark-O and he left the room. Just then Father came in early from the accounting office where he worked. He had a grocery bag that he handed to Barbie. It was full of TV dinners.

"Please start the oven and put these in," he said to her. He took off his coat and went into the bedroom. Julie came out and he shut the door.

Julie set the table, and when the oven was hot, Barbie put in the dinners. Neither one said a word, and Mark-O, who was full of questions, could not think just exactly what it was he really wanted to know, so he too was quiet.

Stephen came in from basketball practice. "I'm hungry," he announced. "What's for supper—TV dinners? You've got to be kidding!"

"Never mind—there's two for you, big boy," said Barbie, who thought his appetite was disgusting. She was secretly hungry all the time, herself. But she was afraid she was going to get fat, so she never ate much at the table.

"Why TV dinners? Is Momma sick or something?" Stephen wondered.

"No, Maryanne is worse. The doctor was just here. He thinks . . ." Barbie's words seemed to stick in her throat, and she didn't finish.

"She's going to go away tonight," said Mark-O, who had found his tongue again.

"Really?" asked Stephen in a whisper.

"Really," said Barbie.

Stephen, who never said much, said nothing now. He walked around the room trying to decide whether to go upstairs and take a shower or go in the living room and turn on the TV. Finally he turned on the TV very softly, but didn't look at it. Mark-O went in and sat down beside him in the easy chair.

"Do you feel bad, too?" he asked.

"Yeah, I feel awful." Stephen's voice cracked and went clear down in his chest.

CHAPTER FIVE

W HEN BARBIE called the family to dinner, Stephen discovered he was not hungry anymore. Neither was anyone else, so Barbie cleared away the half-empty aluminum plates and put Stephen's extra dinner in the icebox. Julie gave the leftovers to the dogs.

About eight o'clock, Barbie said, "Mother, it's time for Mark-O and Julie to go to bed."

"Never mind, Barbie," Mother replied. "They can stay up later tonight."

Julie and Mark-O felt an uncomfortable twinge. Something very unusual had to happen before they could stay up. During the next hour Father read them two stories, and they played a game of checkers, which Julie was teaching Mark-O. Barbie and Stephen were trying to study, but they seemed nervous and jumpy.

"Julie, what do you suppose is going to happen?" Mark-O asked.

"I don't know," she answered.

A few minutes later, Father came out of the bedroom and said, "I think you should come in and say good-bye to Maryanne, now."

They all went in and stood around the bed. Maryanne looked just as she had before dinner. But there was a strange feeling in the room. It was like the feeling you get in your stomach when you are waiting for the dentist, only it wasn't just in their stomachs. It seemed to be all around.

One by one, each of the children went up and kissed Maryanne on the cheek. No one told them to. It was as if they knew what to do. First Barbie, then Stephen, then Julie, then Mark-O.

The room was very warm, but when Mark-O kissed Maryanne, her cheek felt quite cool. "Good-bye," he said inside himself. He was sure that he heard her answer, "Good-bye, Mark-O," inside herself. Then he thought she opened her eyes a crack and looked at him. The tiniest smile curled at the corner of her mouth.

He went back to the foot of the bed. It was so silent you could hear Maryanne's breathing, even though it was very soft now. Mark-O thought everyone else had stopped breathing, and he even thought he had. Suddenly, Maryanne was not breathing either.

For a long time, for many minutes, it was quiet. Then, all of a sudden, sound turned back on. Mark-O could hear the usual creakings and noises, the cars outside, the dogs barking, the refrigerator motor starting up. He felt as though he had waked up from a dream—almost.

Everyone moved slowly, like statues that had become alive. A huge white moth rose gently from somewhere near the bed and flew up to the ceiling. It fluttered around for a few seconds, found the window, which Mother had just opened, and glided out into the night. Mark-O watched it go.

Later, in the kitchen, Mother boiled water and made big mugs of instant cocoa. Her eyes were red from crying. She poured a little cream in the cocoa to cool it down, and dropped marshmallows in—two big ones in each cup. Father put bread in the toaster and got out the butter. Then he called Julie, who had locked herself in the bathroom again. She had been crying too, but she came out and sat down at the table with everyone else.

"Go ahead and cry, honey, if you want to," Father said. "You'll have plenty of company. But drink some cocoa, anyway, it will feel good."

Mark-O wanted to cry too, but he looked at Stephen first. He wondered if Stephen would, but he didn't. So Mark-O didn't either. But he started to shake all over, inside and out, and he couldn't stop.

Father sat him on his lap and put cocoa in front of him. "How about a piece of toast, Mark-O?" he asked.

The cocoa was comforting, and pretty soon Mark-O was not shaking anymore. The room was warm and all the lights were on. The group around the table seemed smaller than usual, but it was very close. The emptiness and the lonely feeling were, for the moment, left back in the bedroom, which Mark-O did not want to think about. For some reason, he was just terribly, awfully, unexplainably glad that they were all there in the dining room around the table.

Later, in his bed, Mark-O cried until his pillow was wet. It lasted a long time. Sometime before he went to sleep, he heard a car pull up, the door open and shut, and some people come up the walk. There was talking and moving around downstairs for quite a while, and somebody left, and more people came. Finally he went to sleep.

CHAPTER SIX

W<small>HEN MARK-O</small> came down to breakfast it was late, and Julie pulled him into a corner and whispered, "We don't have to go to school today. And do you know what? Maryanne is not in her bedroom. You ask Momma why. Okay?"

"No. She went away," said Mark-O. Then he remembered it wasn't that kind of going away. But he didn't want to ask Mother any more than Julie did.

They went to the table and neither one talked all

through the meal. They were worried. Mother did not talk, either. Her eyes were still red and puffy, and she sighed every few bites. Barbie and Stephen did not come to the table at all.

After breakfast, Mark-O tried to look into Maryanne's room without anyone watching him.

"I wonder if she is really gone," he said to himself. "Maybe it didn't really happen and she is still there and awake."

He stood in the door and looked at the empty bed and remembered all over again what had happened the night before. Only now it was even more like a dream. He looked at the caterpillar jar—the cocoon was cracked open. Going closer, he saw that it was empty. So that was where the white moth came from!

"Want to talk about something, Mark-O?" asked Father from behind him.

Mark-O jumped. "Ye-e-es. Where . . .?"

"She is at the funeral home, Mark-O. She will stay there until day after tomorrow, and then there will be a funeral. Right now, you and I are going shopping for groceries because there will be people coming to visit."

They bought bags and bags of groceries and when they got home, Aunt Shelley from Salt Lake City was there. Mark-O had seen her only once before in his life, two Christmases ago. Aunt Shell was cleaning and cooking

and talking all at once as fast as she could, which was fast.

In the afternoon, the minister from their church four blocks away came to call. Aunt Shell served coffee and cookies and everyone sat in the living room. First the minister talked to Mother and Father about the funeral service and what music they wanted and a number of things that Mark-O did not listen to. Then he asked everyone to bow his head while he said a prayer. "Father in Heaven, comfort Julie and Mark-O and Barbie and Stephen and their parents with the knowledge that life never ends—it just changes. Amen."

"Is that really true?" Mark-O asked him.

"That is what *I* believe," replied the minister. "I believe that when people die they step through a door into another place that we can't see with our eyes."

"Could they go through a window, too?" asked Mark-O, remembering the moth.

"Yes. Windows let in light, and I believe there is light where people go. But not the kind of light you see with your eyes. It is more like the kind you feel inside when you love someone, like Maryanne."

After the minister left, friends of Mother and Father came. Many were neighbors, most of whom had never been inside the Foss house before. It seemed to Mark-O and Julie that suddenly the family had a large number of friends that they had not known about. Everybody got served coffee and cookies.

The next day Mark-O, Julie, Barbie, and Stephen all went to school. Mark-O was glad. All those people and all that talking had begun to bother him. When he got out on the playground at recess, he ran faster, yelled louder, and played harder than he had ever done before. When he went home he was happy until he got to his porch. There were more people in the house! How he hated all these people! It was his house. Why wouldn't they leave him alone? He could hear them laughing, too.

He went in and stomped loudly up the stairs. When Mother called him down to lunch, he did not answer. She came up after him, but when she saw how angry he looked, she sat down on the bed with him and asked him what was the matter.

"Why don't you tell those people to go home? I can't play the record player and I can't get out the game box and I can't beat my drums and I can't. . ."

"Mark-O, don't you know why all these people are here?"

"They want to talk and laugh and make noise. Anyway, they shouldn't be laughing when Maryanne is dead." Mark-O started to cry.

"Mark-O, you must try to understand. These people are our friends. It is because they are our friends that they are here. They really feel as sad as we do, but they're able to think of cheerful things to say when we can't."

Mark-O tried to understand, because he wanted to please Mother. It was not easy, but then he remembered how comforting it had been sitting around the table drinking cocoa the night Maryanne left, and how glad he had been for his family then. He remembered, too, how this very morning he had laughed and played at school.

"Okay, Momma, it's all right for you to enjoy your friends. But I don't have to, do I?"

"No," said Mother, "but you should come down and enjoy your lunch, anyway."

CHAPTER SEVEN

NEXT MORNING, none of the children went to school. There was a heavy feeling in the house, as though something strange was about to happen.

They all got dressed in their best clothes and sat in the living room, waiting for the time to go to the funeral. Mark-O's stomach was hurting again. He had never been to a funeral and he *knew* he would not like it. The night before, Julie had whispered to him that this was when they would bury Maryanne in the ground. He remembered how cold the ground was this time of year and it worried him.

"Do I have to go?" he asked Mother.

"Yes, you do," she replied firmly. "Anyway, it will not last very long. You will feel better if you go. Remember how you always bury guinea pigs when they die? You read poems when you put them in the ground, and you say a prayer. Then you feel better. This will be like that."

Mark-O looked at Stephen to see how he felt. "I don't like getting dressed up, either, but we have to be men, you know," Stephen said.

Mark-O was puzzled to see a smile appear on Father's face, as though Stephen had said something funny. But he decided he had better act at least as grown-up as Stephen.

Father looked at his watch and got up. There was a vase of tiny white rosebuds on the coffee table. Father handed one bud to each of the children. "Take good care of them," he said. "You will need them later."

They put on their coats and walked together down the street to the church. Inside, the organ was playing. An usher took them to a front section of seats which had been roped off with a red silk cord. He let them in and removed the cord. Other people were coming in the back. Mark-O saw many whom he knew—there was even the principal of his school, where Maryanne had gone too, but only for half days in the first grade.

Then Mark-O looked at the front of the church. There were more flowers than he had ever seen in one place. And there was a strange white box right in the middle in front of the altar. It had a blue cloth over it. Mark-O was going to ask what was in it, but he had the uncomfortable feeling that he knew.

The organ stopped playing and the minister, who now had a long black robe on, got up to speak. He talked about Maryanne and Mark-O tried to listen. It wasn't easy. The air in the church was stuffy, and besides his right leg was going to sleep. When he wriggled it, Aunt Shell gave him a stern look.

Then the minister read long passages out of the Bible. They were hard to understand because of the long words. Finally there was a prayer and the minister sat down again.

Father got up and motioned to the children to follow him. They filed out of the church and were put into the station wagon of a friend of Father's. Mother and Aunt Shell got in with them, but Father went off and got into a long, very black car at the side of the church. Mark-O could see several men carrying the white box out and putting it into the back of the black car. By that time, all of the people had left the church, and the black car started down the driveway. The station wagon pulled out right after it. Mark-O could see the other cars following them.

"That's a *hearse*," whispered Julie, who had been to a funeral before. "All the people follow it to the graveyard with their lights on."

"Why?" asked Mark-O.

"So people will know this is a funeral and will let all the cars go together even if there is a red light."

Mark-O had the strange feeling that everything that was happening was part of a Big Law that had to be obeyed. You could see all these unpleasant things getting ready to happen, but you couldn't keep them from happening. Even if you could, he guessed you wouldn't, because you would have to stay behind while the rest of the family went on and that would be worse.

"I wish I could run away," he whispered to Julie.

"Me, too," agreed Julie, "except I want to put my rose on the coffin."

Mark-O looked at his rose. The stem was bent in one place and it looked wilted because he had held it inside his hand too long.

"What's it for?" he asked Julie.

"We put it on the coffin before it's buried—it's like giving it to Maryanne."

"Oh."

When the cars arrived at the cemetery, the people followed the family to a place where a hole had been dug.

A huge pile of dirt was beside it, covered with a green plastic cloth. Some men carried the coffin over and set it down next to the hole, and removed the blue cloth. The minister stood beside it and the family gathered around. He opened a little book and began to read.

"Dust to dust, earth to earth . . . ," he read.

"Is that what you meant about William being part of the ground?" Mark-O whispered to Julie.

"I guess so," said Julie.

". . . We commend her spirit to Heaven and her body to the earth from whence it came," finished the minister.

Father whispered to the children, "Now you may go over and put your roses on the coffin if you wish to."

Mark-O, Stephen, and Julie, and Barbie together placed their roses on the coffin. Four men carefully let the

coffin down into the hole and some other men took the green cover off the dirt.

Mother took Mark-O's hand and went to the station wagon, followed by the rest of the family. Barbie, Julie, and Mother cried all the way home, and Father sat in the front seat alone, not talking to anyone, even the friend who was driving. Stephen sat with Mark-O in the little second back seat where there was only room for two. Mark-O stuck his hand in Stephen's pocket and looked out the window. Stephen put his arm around Mark-O, and they looked out the window together.

CHAPTER EIGHT

ALL THE children went back to school the next day
and Father went back to work at his office. Aunt Shell
left with Father, who was to drop her off at the bus
station so she could go home to her job. The funeral
seemed like something that had happened last year instead of yesterday.

The house was still and empty. Mark-O did not have to
leave for two hours. Again, he had the feeling that if he
went into Maryanne's room she would be there. He

walked by and looked in the door, but of course she wasn't. He went out onto the porch, hoping he might see something interesting. But there was no Maryanne to take it to, even if he found something. He went back inside and sat on the davenport.

Mother came in with the vacuum cleaner. The rug was a mess after all the company.

"Well, Mark-O," she said, "you are very quiet today. Is something wrong?"

"I just want Maryanne back."

"Yes, I know," sighed Mother, sitting down beside him. "We all miss her." She gave him a hug.

"Why did she go away?"

"That is something I don't know for sure, Mark-O, but some people do not seem to be meant to live very long."

"Then why was Maryanne born?"

Mother thought for a while before she answered. "Maryanne was very happy in our family. Everyone was good to her and she was someone very special. You did not give anyone else presents every day, did you? And you did not walk quietly in anyone else's room because they were sleeping. But lately I have noticed that you are learning to be more thoughtful of other people as well."

Mother ruffled Mark-O's hair. "We all learned many things from Maryanne," she said. "Mostly, I guess, how much we appreciate our family."

56

Mark-O was pleased—he *did* understand what Mother was saying.

Mother smiled. "Maryanne was like the plants in our garden," she said. "They only last a short while, but they make us happy while they are here."

That reminded Mark-O of something. "Momma! I forgot all about my seeds! Did you water them?"

"Yes, and I forgot to tell you this morning, but something is happening to them."

Mark-O ran to the kitchen. One plant was already up, with two fat green leaves. Another was just breaking the surface—a little mound cracked open at the top revealed a piece of green leaf curled up inside. The larger plant had a piece of the old seed fastened to it. The seed was black and crumbly like the one he had dug up.

"Oh, Momma!" Mark-O called. "I promised the first plant to Maryanne. It didn't come up in time!"

"Don't feel too badly about that," said Mother, following him into the kitchen. "When it gets bigger we can plant it outside and call it our 'Maryanne Tree.' "

That would be nice, thought Mark-O. Maybe the white moth would come and sit in it. "When will it grow bigger?" he asked.

"Perhaps next year, if you water it well," answered Mother.

A year was too long. "I want to do it *now*," Mark-O

said, loudly and clearly.

"The plant isn't ready. You'll have to take care of it until it is," Mother explained.

An idea was stirring inside Mark-O, but he didn't know what it was, yet. There was something he wanted to do. Something for Maryanne?

He stood on one foot, looking at the tiny tree. He was thinking about it growing tall as the house. Inside his mind he could see its branches bending in the wind and halfway up was the moth.

The moth is already grown up, he thought. I don't have to wait for it a whole year. But it's gone away, like Maryanne has gone away.

Suddenly, as he remembered the moth, the idea came clear. He ran from the kitchen, up the stairs, and into his room.

CHAPTER NINE

Mark-o got out his crayons, paper, and paint set. First he drew a moth with white crayon on the white paper. Then he took blue water color and washed it over the whole page. When it dried, the moth stood out against the blue as though it were flying in the night.

He had learned how to make this kind of picture in school, but he had never done one by himself before. Now, as he looked at it, he thought it was the most beautiful picture he had ever seen. He could hardly believe he had done it. It made him sad, but it made him happy, too.

He raced downstairs with the picture and fastened it with Scotch tape to the wall at the back of a small table in the entryway. He could hardly work fast enough, he was in such a hurry. Then he ran to the jar with the cocoon and the cup of plants and set them on the table in front of the picture.

That afternoon, after school, Mark-O waited in the living room for Julie. Barbie came in first. When she saw the picture, she exclaimed, "Mark-O! Did you do that? It's beautiful! It looks like the moth . . ."

"It is," interrupted Mark-O. "Did you see it, too?"

"Oh, yes, and it startled me."

"How come?"

"I guess because it happened right when Maryanne died. It made me feel—well—like it was Maryanne."

Later, when Julie came in, the first thing *she* saw was the plant in the cup. "Oh, your seed is up! And look, there's the old dead seed on the leaf!"

"Yes," said Mark-O. "Barbie told me the seed had to crumble up so the plant inside could grow."

Then Julie pointed to the picture. "Is that the butterfly out of your cocoon?"

"Yes, only it's a moth."

"Let's get some white paper," Julie said.

"For what?"

"You'll see." She and Mark-O went to his room to find the white paper. Julie cut a large square hole in the paper that just fitted the picture. She fastened it over the picture, which then had a white frame.

Julie stood looking at the picture after they had hung it back up. "You know," she said, "it looks like a fairy story picture—like a *magic* moth. I saw it, too, that night."

After a while, Stephen came in. The entryway was empty now. When he saw the picture, he stood a long while in front of it. Father came home while he was standing there.

"Dad, where do you suppose Mark-O got an idea like that?" Stephen asked.

"Mark-O's still young enough to ask questions and really look at things," said Father.

"I guess you got a point. Even if I do get tired of his questions sometimes." Stephen looked at the picture again.

Just then Mother came in from the kitchen to see who was talking in the front hall.

Father turned to her and said, "This picture of Mark-O's is unusual."

"I know," replied Mother. "And he has been so quiet

today—not at all himself. It *is* strange about that moth coming out of the cocoon when it did. Except that Maryanne seemed so cold that I had turned up the heat, and the room was unusually warm that evening. That could have done it, I suppose."

Barbie had been in the study showing Julie how to do an arithmetic problem. Hearing voices by the front door, they both came out to see what was happening.

"How long before dinner, Momma?" Julie asked.

"Nearly an hour," Mother replied. "The cake is still in the oven."

Mark-O came down from his room to find his whole family standing in front of his picture. It reminded him of the night they had all stood around Maryanne's bed to say good-bye, only there was a difference. They were not saying good-bye this time. They were beginning to remember Maryanne forever.

If Maryanne was here. Mark-O thought, she would make up the beginning of a story about my picture. It would go like this: "Once upon a time there was a caterpillar that spun a cocoon and one day . . ."

If you had looked in the dining room window of the George Foss home an hour later, you would have seen Father, Stephen, Barbie, Julie, and Mark-O sitting around the table finishing their dinner. It was the 9th of

March and Mother had just returned from the kitchen with a pale green cake sprinkled with peanuts.

"Oh!" screeched Mark-O. "It's my favorite cake!"

"Well, then, Mark-O, whose cake shall this be?" asked Mother.

Mark-O thought and thought.

"We've had all the guinea pigs," said Julie.

"And all the cats," said Barbie.

"And the dogs," said Stephen.

It's about time for Maryanne's birthday, thought Mark-O, but it made him feel bad so he did not say it aloud. He wondered if the others remembered.

Everyone was silent, waiting for Mark-O to decide on the birthday. The electric clock on the wall hummed loudly.

"I guess," said Mark-O finally, "that it's the moth's birthday."

"You made a good choice," said Father. "Now you may light the candle."

Mark-O had never been allowed to light a candle at the table and he felt very grand and important as he struck the match on the side of the box. It lit on the first strike, as though he had always lit candles for the cakes. Carefully, he held the match to the candle, then blew it out and laid it on his plate. He waited for someone to start singing "Happy Birthday," but no one did.

"I guess," said Father, "that we can't sing yet, but perhaps we will next year. Let's all blow the candle out together, instead."

Everyone took a huge breath and blew hard. The candle went out and Mother began to cut the cake. The first piece was a large one and she handed it to Mark-O.

P   Lee, Virginia
Le   The magic moth

DATE			

AM 4956